METHUEN'S MONOGRAPHS
ON CHEMICAL SUBJECTS

━━

General Editors:
H. J. EMELÉUS, F.R.S., D. W. G. STYLE
and R. P. BELL, F.R.S.

ATOMIC STRUCTURE
AND CHEMICAL BONDING

Atomic Structure
and Chemical Bonding

A NON-MATHEMATICAL
INTRODUCTION

FRITZ SEEL, *1915-*
University of Saarbrücken

Translated from the fourth German edition
and revised by

N. N. Greenwood and H. P. Stadler
University of Newcastle upon Tyne

LONDON: METHUEN & CO LTD
NEW YORK: JOHN WILEY & SONS INC

First published in Germany in 1961 *as*
Atombau und Chemische Bindung
© *Ferdinand Enke Verlag*, 1961
This translation first published in Great Britain in 1963
© *Methuen & Co Ltd*, 1963
Printed in Great Britain by
Spottiswoode Ballantyne Ltd, London and Colchester
Catalogue No. 2/2663/11

Contents

Foreword to English Edition

Seel's *Atombau und Chemische Bindung* which was first published in 1956 has now reached its 4th German edition and has already been translated into several languages. Professor Seel's intention was to write a concise, straightforward account of the modern theory of chemical bonding which would give both perspective and significance to this subject for students taking it up for the first time. The immediate and continuing popularity of his book on the Continent testifies to the success with which he has achieved this aim. The treatment is non-mathematical and relies on the skilful use of simple pictorial models. In order to emphasize the essential unity of chemical theory the subject matter has been divided not according to the traditional fields of chemistry (inorganic, organic, and physical) but according to the four basic types of chemical bonding – ionic, covalent, metallic, and intermolecular. Modern concepts such as ligand field theory and charge transfer complexes have been introduced with a simplicity and directness which will undoubtedly stimulate the reader to delve further into these subjects.

A novel feature for English readers is the discussion of chemical reactivity in terms of bonding theory, and the Author has introduced many important ideas of his own into this section of the book. The relation between chemical bonding and physical properties such as hardness, conductivity and colour is also well handled.

In preparing this edition the Translators have, with the Author's consent, modified the text slightly in a few places, and have also made some minor corrections and additions. It is their belief that the book provides an excellent introduction to modern ideas of atomic structure and chemical bonding. A bibliography for further reading is provided at the end of the book.

N N G

February, 1963   H P S

PART 1

Atomic Structure

1. The structure of extranuclear electrons

An understanding of the nature of chemical bonding depends on a knowledge of atomic structure. Atoms are composed of electrically charged particles: a positively charged *nucleus* and up to about 100 negative 'atoms of electricity' or *electrons*. In a neutral atom the total charge on the electrons just balances the charge of the nucleus. If there are fewer electrons the atom has a net positive charge; if there are more electrons the net charge is negative. Such electrically charged atoms are called *ions*.

In order to discuss the energy of such systems it is necessary to define a uniquely determined standard state. To do this let us consider that the atom is completely separated into its component nucleus and electrons; the particles should be at rest and so far apart that all the work necessary for their separation has been performed. In the simplest case, the hydrogen atom, there is a nucleus and one electron. The system in this state has *potential energy* (or energy of position) because the particles have been separated against their attractive forces, but no *kinetic energy* (energy of movement) since they are at rest.

When an atom is built up from the separated particles the initial potential energy of the system diminishes because the distance between the oppositely charged particles decreases. Potential energy is thereby gained but not all of this is available as binding energy since the particles cannot remain at rest. Motion is necessary for a stable atomic system to ensure that the electrons do not fall into the nucleus which attracts them. To a first approximation we can assume that the atomic nucleus, which contains almost the entire mass of the atom, remains at rest and that the electrons are set in motion. To achieve this electronic motion, some of the potential energy which is liberated when the nucleus and the electrons combine must be converted into kinetic energy. The exact proportion depends on the type of interaction between the particles and in the case of electrical interaction it amounts to one-half. The remainder of the energy can be considered as the *energy of formation* of the atom from the initial standard state. This is shown in Figure 1.

At one time it was thought that electrons moved round the atomic nucleus in exactly prescribed circular or elliptical orbits in the same way that planets move round the sun (the *Bohr–Sommerfeld* model of

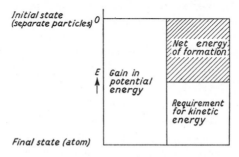

FIG. 1. Conversion of energy during the formation of atoms.

the atom). However it is not possible to assign precise orbits to the electrons because it is not possible to define simultaneously both the position and the velocity of particles as small as electrons (*Heisenberg uncertainty principle*). Nevertheless the movement of the electrons is not completely arbitrary and they occupy certain preferred regions of space around the nucleus.

To a first approximation these regions of space can be regarded as a system of cells which surround the nucleus. The electrons in each cell trace out a particular pattern or *orbital* which imparts specific properties to the chemical elements. The orbitals are grouped into shells which are named K, L, M, N . . . and numbered 1, 2, 3, 4 . . . . The number of the shell is called the *principal quantum number*, n. Orbitals in each shell are further divided into *subshells* designated by the symbols s, p, d, f, depending on the values of a second quantum number, l, the *orbital quantum number*, which has the values 0, 1, 2, 3 respectively. Whether letters or numbers are used in a particular context is merely a matter of convention; their relationship may be summarized as follows:

Principal quantum number, n	Orbital quantum number, l
$1 \leftrightarrow K$	$0 \leftrightarrow s$
$2 \leftrightarrow L$	$1 \leftrightarrow p$
$3 \leftrightarrow M$	$2 \leftrightarrow d$
$4 \leftrightarrow N$	$3 \leftrightarrow f$

Thus a $3p$-electron is one for which $n = 3$ and $l = 1$; it is in the M-shell.

The total number of orbitals in a given shell K, L, M etc., is $Z_n = n^2$, and in each shell the number of orbitals of any one type s, p, d etc., is given by $Z_l = (2l+1)$. The number of values of l is limited by the relation $l \leqslant n-1$. Thus, the K-shell consists of a single orbital, the L-shell

TABLE 1

The structure of extranuclear electron clouds

Electron shell	n	$l \leqslant n-1$	Type of orbital	Number of orbitals $Z_n = n^2$
K	1	0	s	1
L	2	0, 1	s, p	$1+3 = 4$
M	3	0, 1, 2	s, p, d	$1+3+5 = 9$
N	4	0, 1, 2, 3	s, p, d, f	$1+3+5+7 = 16$

contains four orbitals and the M-shell nine. This can be seen in the following way, For the K-shell n is 1 and there is therefore only one possible value of l namely 0. For the L-shell, n is 2 so that l can be 0 or 1; the case $l = 0$ corresponds to an s-orbital; for $l = 1$, $Z_l = 3$ so there are three p-orbitals. For the M-shell, n is 3 and so l can take on the values 0, 1, or 2. The M-shell therefore consists of an s-orbital, three p-orbitals and five d-orbitals, $(l = 2, Z_l = 5)$. These numerical relations are summarized in Table 1 and are represented schematically in Figure 2a.

To complete the description of the electron we also need information about its *spin*. This is perhaps best understood by considering the electron as a small sphere which is capable of rotation in either direction about an axis (see Figure 2*b*). The concept of electron spin allows us to develop a theory of the magnetic properties of matter. One can imagine that the self-rotation of the electrons produces circular electric currents which in turn produce a magnetic field like that of an electromagnet; this field can align itself in the direction of

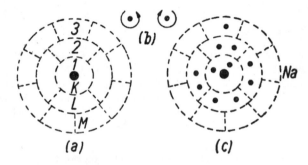

Fig. 2. Schematic representation of the structure of extranuclear electron-shells.

the lines of force of an external magnetic field in such a way as to enhance the external field considerably (*paramagnetism*). Paramagnetism is also occasionally produced by the orbital motion of the *p*-, *d*-, *f*-electrons providing this is not cancelled by a corresponding electron with opposed movement. If pairs of electrons spin in opposite directions with equal velocity their magnetic fields will cancel out. An external magnetic field produces orientation in this case also, the self-rotation in one direction being accelerated and in the other retarded so as to weaken slightly the external field (*diamagnetism*).

It is found that two electrons in an atom never have the same detailed *distribution patterns*; i.e. each orbital can only be occupied by at most two electrons and these must then spin in opposite directions. The spins are then said to be *antiparallel*. This rule, the so-called *Pauli exclusion principle*, immediately leads to the possible electron distributions within an atom. For example, the most stable electronic arrangement for the sodium atom is shown schematically in Figure 2c.

2. The Aufbau principle

The distribution pattern of an electron influences considerably the energy of formation of an atom. For an atom or ion with a single extranuclear electron e.g., H, He^+, Li^{2+} etc., the energy of formation is determined only by the principal quantum number n of the shell which

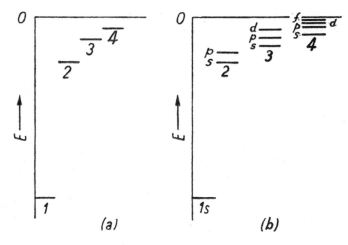

FIG. 3. Sequence of electron energy-levels (*a*) for the hydrogen atom, (*b*) for an atom with several electrons.

the electron occupies (see Figure 3a). Thus $E_n = E_1/n^2$ where E_1 is the energy value for $n = 1$. For 1 gram atom of hydrogen (that is $6 \cdot 02 \times 10^{23}$ hydrogen atoms) E_1 has the value 312 kcal. E_n decreases rapidly with increasing n since $E_1 : E_2 : E_3 \ldots$ varies as $1 : \frac{1}{4} : \frac{1}{9} \ldots$. It can be seen that for a one-electron atom the various orbitals which are distinguished by the symbols s, p, d, f within a given shell all have the same energy. Such energy levels are said to be *degenerate*.

In atoms containing more than one electron the energy levels are no longer independent of the orbital quantum number, l. The sequence of energy levels within the atom then follows the sequence $(n+l)$, and if two configurations lead to an equal numerical value for $(n+l)$ then the one with the lower n-value is the more stable. Thus, in any shell, an electron in an s-orbital has a lower energy than one in a p- or

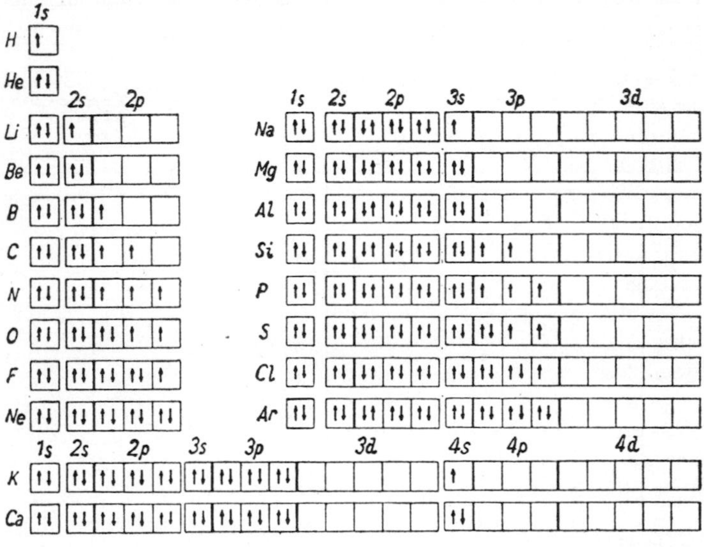

FIG. 4. Ground states of elements from hydrogen to calcium.

d-orbital. This is shown in Figure 3b from which it can also be seen that the energy level for a $4s$-orbital $(n+l=4)$ is less than that for a $3d$-orbital $(n+l=5)$.

This method of building up a sequence of energy levels for the extranuclear electrons is called the *Aufbau Principle*. If each orbital is doubly occupied in the correct sequence until the nuclear charge is just compensated by the electron charges, the *ground state* or lowest energy state of the atom is obtained. If an electron distribution does not correspond to the ground state, the atom can radiate energy and thereby return to the ground state; conversely it can absorb more energy and thereby become 'excited' into a state of still higher energy. In terms of the symbolism just developed, and using superscripts to denote the number of electrons in a given orbital, the ground state and one of the *excited states* of a carbon atom can be represented as follows:

$$C: 1s^2\, 2s^2\, 2p^2, \quad C^*: 1s^2\, 2s\, 2p^3$$

In Figure 4 the details of the ground states of the first twenty atoms are given. The orbitals are depicted as small squares and each electron is symbolized by an arrow to indicate the direction of the spin. Figure 4 also illustrates a further point, namely that degenerate electron states (electron states which have the same energy) only become doubly occupied after each has first been singly occupied, and electrons in the singly occupied orbitals have their spins aligned parallel (cf. page 12).

The electronic ground states of all the elements and their relative energies are presented schematically in Figure 5. Both Figure 4 and Figure 5 give a clear impression of the periodicity which results from the progressive occupation of the electron shells. We are thus led to the *Periodic Table* of the elements which was established one hundred years ago by *Mendeleev, Meyer*, and others who observed regularities in the properties of the elements.

3. The shape of orbitals

In order to discuss the nature of the chemical bond it is necessary to have some knowledge of the detailed structure or shape of orbitals. Atomic orbitals have exactly the same shapes as the patterns generated by a pulsating dust-cloud which is confined within an elastic sphere. However, it is simpler to consider first an analogous two-dimensional system, e.g. a vibrating circular membrane such as the skin of a drum. If the membrane is covered with a fine powder and the drum is struck, the membrane divides into regions separated by lines (so-called *nodal lines*) along which the powder accumulates since the membrane does not vibrate there. Some of the possible *modes of*

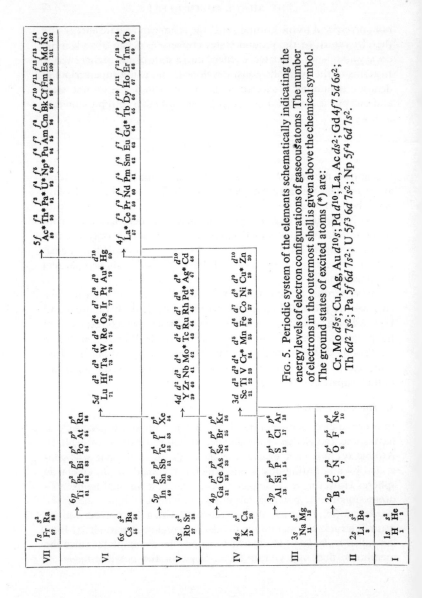

Fig. 5. Periodic system of the elements schematically indicating the energy levels of electron configurations of gaseous atoms. The number of electrons in the outermost shell is given above the chemical symbol. The ground states of excited atoms (*) are:

Cr, Mo d^5s; Cu, Ag, Au $d^{10}s$; Pd d^{10}; La, Ac ds^2; Gd $4f^7 5d 6s^2$; Th $6d^2 7s^2$; Pa $5f 6d 7s^2$; U $5f^3 6d 7s^2$; Np $5f^4 6d 7s^2$.

vibration of a circular membrane are shown in Figure 6 from which it is clear that the nodal lines can be either concentric circles or diameters. Each vibrational state of the membrane is characterized by the number of nodal lines and their type. If we call the total number of nodes including the edge of the membrane n and the total number of nodal lines l we obtain the notation given in Figure 6. For instance, the top left-hand membrane has only one circular node so that $n = 1$ and $l = 0$ whereas the membrane in the lower right-hand

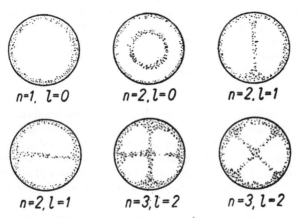

$n=1, \ l=0$　　　$n=2, l=0$　　　$n=2, l=1$

$n=2, l=1$　　　$n=3, l=2$　　　$n=3, l=2$

FIG. 6. Independent modes of vibration of a circular membrane.

corner of Figure 6 has three nodes ($n = 3$) of which two are linear ($l = 2$). Once again we have the relationship $l \leqslant n - 1$. There are, in fact, an infinite number of vibrational modes for each given number of linear nodes since the patterns on the membrane can always be rotated by any arbitrary amount. However, all such vibrational modes can be built up by the appropriate superposition of two independent modes and Figure 6 shows only these independent modes.

In passing from a two-dimensional membrane to the three-dimensional pulsating sphere it is necessary to replace the circular nodes by concentric *spherical nodes* and the linear nodes by *nodal planes* which pass through the centre of the sphere. Again the total number of nodes including the outer spherical shell is called n and for each value of n there is a finite number of independent vibrational modes. However, for a given number of spherical and planar nodes the number of independent vibrations is no longer two as in the case of the circular membrane but is $(2l+1)$ where l, the total number of planar nodes, must again be $\leqslant n-1$.

Our model of the atom is closely related to the pulsating spherical dust-cloud. Each pattern into which the pulsating dust-cloud can be subdivided corresponds to an orbital and each independent mode of vibration corresponds to an electronic state of the atom. In this way we obtain a pictorial interpretation of the quantum numbers n and l with which we have numbered the electron shells and orbitals, and we can see how it comes about that a shell is composed of n^2 orbitals and a sub-shell of $(2l+1)$ orbitals respectively.

4. ψ-functions

An extranuclear electron can be regarded as an electrical charge distribution which surrounds the nucleus like a *cloud*. The shapes of the clouds formed by the individual electrons are determined by the structure of the orbitals whose nodes subdivide the charge cloud. In Figure 7 the shapes of the s-, p-, and d-orbitals are represented pictorially. The shaded areas indicate the regions of space in which there is the greatest *probability* of finding the electrons characterized by $l = 0, 1,$ and 2 respectively. The $+$ and $-$ signs refer to the sign of the so-called ψ-function. In the case of the pulsating spherical dust-cloud this function gives the amplitude of vibration of a dust particle from its mean position as specified by the coordinates x, y, z. In the atomic model ψ is a mathematical function such that $\psi^2_{n,l} \Delta V$ gives the probability of finding an electron in the small element of volume ΔV, the electron being characterized by the quantum numbers n and l. For the $1s$-, $2s$-, and $2p$-orbitals the variation of ψ along the x-axis is shown in Figure 7.

We see that the s-electron cloud is spherical, the p-cloud resembles a dumb-bell, and the d-cloud a rosette. The coordinate symbols x, y, z have been chosen deliberately as the subscripts to distinguish the three p-clouds since these each have the same shape but differ in their orientation in space. In the corresponding ψ-functions, x, y, z appear as factors which destroy the spherical symmetry of the electron cloud and the same is true for the subscripts used to distinguish the d-electrons. The remaining part of the ψ-function depends only on the

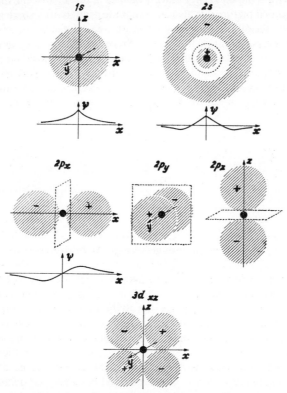

FIG. 7. Orbital shapes for extranuclear electrons.

distance r of the point x, y, z from the nucleus. Hence, the *charge density distribution* of an electron in a p_x-orbital, for example, is greatest in the direction of the x-axis and drops to zero in the yz-plane ($x = 0$).

More precisely, each electron cloud extends to infinity, but the probability of finding the electron at increasing distances from the nucleus becomes vanishingly small so that effectively each atom only occupies a small and fairly sharply defined region of space. From this more refined picture it is also clear that the orbitals are superimposed one upon the other and are not adjacent to each other as suggested by the naïve representation in Figure 2. Since all electrons are negatively charged they repel each other and this influences markedly both their pattern of movement and their energy. However, the overall shape of the electron cloud and the positions of the nodes, which are our main interest in this qualitative picture, are not markedly affected.

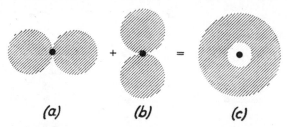

FIG. 8. Superposition of two p-electron clouds.

The ideas which we have now gained about the structure of the extranuclear electrons enable us to interpret various other details of atomic structure. Thus, the fact that all three p-orbitals are first singly occupied before any become doubly occupied, arises from the fact that electrons repel each other and will tend to keep as far apart as possible.

The superposition of two p-electron clouds does not give a rosette-shaped charge distribution like a d-orbital but a ring-shaped charge cloud as shown in Figure 8. The third p-electron cloud fits into this so well that the superposition of all three clouds gives a spherical charge distribution. This can be shown mathematically since the ψ^2-functions of the three p-electrons contain the factors x^2, y^2, and z^2 and the equation for a sphere is $x^2 + y^2 + z^2 = r^2$. It is this spherical symmetry which is responsible, in part, for the special stability of configurations with three or six p-electrons in which the p-subshell is half-full or full.

The position is slightly more complicated for d-orbitals. It is clear from Figure 9 that the three d-electron clouds d_{xy}, d_{xz}, and d_{yz} do not add up to a spherically symmetrical charge cloud since in each case the individual distributions have nodes along their coordinate axes. One might imagine that this deficit could be made up by three further electron clouds oriented as in Figures 9d–f in which the electron

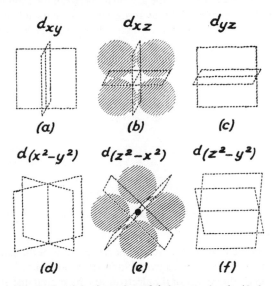

FIG. 9. Spatial orientation of d-electron clouds. (Only the positions of the nodal planes are shown for four of the d-electron states.)

density is greatest along the coordinate axes. A simple calculation on the basis of the given subscripts, however, indicates that this would add too much electronic charge, and it is necessary to multiply the ψ-functions of the $d_{(z^2-x^2)}$- and $d_{(z^2-y^2)}$-electrons by $1/\sqrt{3}$ and to add these reduced functions together in order to obtain the ψ-function of a new electron distribution, $d_{(3z^2-r^2)/\sqrt{3}}$. This is frequently referred to more simply as d_{z^2} and Figure 10 shows a section through this

modified d-orbital. The new electron cloud corresponding to d_{z^2}, together with the $d_{(x^2-y^2)}$-electron cloud and the three clouds from the d_{xy}, d_{xz}, and d_{yz}-functions gives a spherical charge distribution.†
In this way it can be shown that five d-electrons, one in each d-orbital, give rise to a spherically symmetrical electron cloud and that ten d-electrons constitute a fully occupied, spherical d-subshell.

It remains only to explain the similarity between the atomic model and the pulsating sphere. This analogy, which appears at first sight to be remarkable for two systems of such different size, is due to the fact

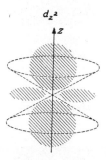

FIG. 10. Modified d-electron cloud.

that both problems involve mathematical equations of the same kind. (The exact motion of the electron within the atom is not important, what matters is the energy of the electron, and its spatial distribution.) The complicated differential equations from which the ψ-functions are calculated were deduced by *Schrödinger* after *de Broglie* had shown that there was a simple relation between the mass and velocity of an electron on the one hand and the wavelength of the hypothetical electron vibrations on the other.

The perceptive reader may have noticed that our atomic model still leaves several questions unanswered: for instance, how does an

† Translators' Footnote. The usual nomenclature for the d-orbitals is as given; the actual functions which appear in the mathematics are $2xy$, $2yz$, $2zx$, x^2-y^2, and $(3z^2-r^2)/\sqrt{3}$. These, when squared and added, give $4r^4/3$ which has spherical symmetry.

electron in a *p*- or *d*-orbital pass through the nodal planes within which the electron density (that is the probability of finding the electron) is zero? The question is answered by the *wave-mechanical model* of the atom due to *Dirac*. According to this model a full description of the movement of an electron requires not one but four ψ-functions and the probability of finding an electron in the volume ΔV is given by the function:

$$(\psi_1^2 + \psi_2^2 + \psi_3^2 + \psi_4^2).\Delta V$$

The set of four ψ-functions always contains simultaneously some *s*- and *p*-, or some *s*-, *p*-, *d*-, or some *p*-, *d*-, *f*- character. As a result, instead of nodes we now have only constrictions in the electron clouds. This more general theory yields twice as many orbitals as the

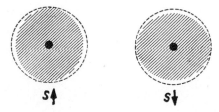

Fig. 11. Electron clouds for the 1*s*-state.

simple one. Thus in place of the spherically symmetrical 1*s*-electron cloud we now obtain two axially distorted, approximately spherical electron clouds which together supplement each other to give an ideal spherical distribution (see Figure 11). On this theory it is possible to dispense with the hypothesis of the spinning electron and there is therefore no difficulty in imagining that, as a free electron approaches an atomic nucleus, it can spread out into a field of matter or electron cloud. Unfortunately, the elegance of this more general theory is bought at the expense of considerably more mathematical effort and for that reason the problems of chemical bonding will be treated in terms of the simpler theory which includes the hypothesis of electron spin.

PART 2

The Nature of the Chemical Bond

The problem of chemical bonding is basically the same as that of atomic structure except that in chemical compounds we have systems in which *several* nuclei are surrounded by electrons in sufficient numbers to balance the charges on the nuclei. Fortunately even this more complicated state of affairs can be treated satisfactorily.

1. Ionic compounds

Salt-like substances, for example compounds having chemical formulae such as NaF, NaCl, MgO, CaF_2 are built up from *monatomic ions*, i.e. from single atoms which carry a surplus positive or negative charge. The charge arises from the fact that in such ions

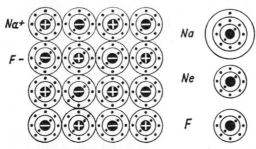

FIG. 12. Schematic representation of the formation of a sodium fluoride crystal. (Note that, in reality, the sodium ions are smaller than the fluoride ions).

the nucleus is surrounded by either a smaller or a larger number of electrons than corresponds to the total nuclear charge. Thus a sodium fluoride crystal consists of positively charged sodium ions (Na^+) and negatively charged fluoride ions (F^-) both of which have the same electronic system as a neutral neon atom (cf. Figure 12). The stoichio-metric composition of such compounds can be deduced from the charges on the ions: e.g. Na^+, Mg^{2+}, Ca^{2+}, F^-, Cl^-, O^{2-}. Chemical bonding results from the attractive forces between the oppositely charged ions. These forces pull the ions together into a regular array

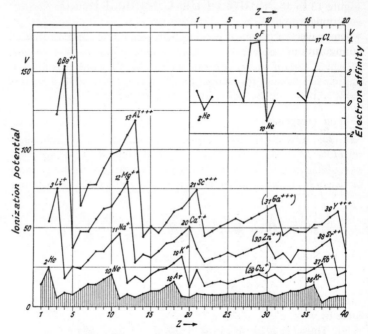

Fig. 13. Ionization potentials and electron affinities in volts
(1 eV per atom = 23 kcal/gram atom).

or *lattice* until the attraction is just balanced by the mutual repulsive forces between the electron clouds surrounding the two types of ion.

Monatomic ions frequently have the same number of electrons as the rare-gas atom which precedes or follows the element in the periodic table. Further examples of ions with the neon electron con-figuration are Mg^{2+} and O^{2-} whereas K^+, Ca^{2+}, and Cl^- have the argon configuration. The prevalence of ions with inert gas configurations reflects the stability of the 8-electron group (s^2p^6) – the *octet rule*. This can be seen clearly from the *ionization potentials* and *electron affinities* of the elements concerned. The ionization potential of an atom or ion is the energy required to remove one electron, and Figure 13 shows that this is a maximum for species having the inert gas configuration. Conversely, the electron affinity, or energy evolved when an electron is added to an atom or ion, is a minimum for these configurations. From this it follows that the ionic charge or *ionic*

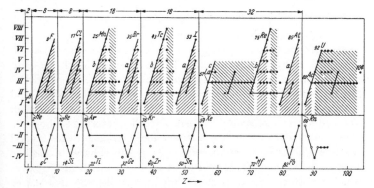

FIG. 14. Stoichiometric valencies of elements towards oxygen ($+$) and hydrogen ($-$).

valency will be determined by the number of places in the periodic table by which these atoms are removed from an inert gas (the octet rule). Thus the fluoride ion and chloride ion have a valency -1 because fluorine and chlorine atoms must gain one valency electron to attain the 8-electron configuration of neon and argon respectively. Similarly the calcium ion has a valency of $+2$ since the calcium atom must lose two electrons to attain the same electronic configuration as argon. The tendency to attain a complete d^{10}-configuration is less marked and this is reflected in the variable valencies of the transition elements where the d-shell is being filled (see Figures 5 and 14).

The energy of formation of an ionic compound depends not only on the ionization potential of the cation and the electron affinity of the anion but also on the energy which is liberated during the formation of the ionic lattice from the individual ions (the *lattice energy*). In addition there are terms involving the energy required to form isolated atoms of the metal and non-metal from the crystals and molecules of the reacting elements. The energy of formation of an ionic compound therefore depends on the sum of five energy terms whose magnitudes must all be measured or estimated before theoretical predictions can be made about the possibility of making the compound.

2. Ionic size and ionic lattices

Although the stoichiometric composition of an ionic compound is determined solely by the charge on its ions, the size of the ions is also important in deciding the detailed lattice structure which the compound adopts. Generally, for a given ionic charge, *ionic size* increases rapidly with increasing atomic number within each group and decreases slightly with increasing atomic number along each period. The well-known *lanthanide contraction* which is observed for both the atomic and the ionic volumes of lanthanide elements provides a good example. Furthermore, an increase in the positive charge of a cation decreases its size markedly because of the increased attractive forces which act on the electron cloud; for anions, the negative charge reduces the attractive force of the nucleus and this results in a considerable expansion of the electron cloud. Figure 15 illustrates the relative sizes of several monatomic ions as determined from measurements of *internuclear distances* in crystal lattices of ionic compounds.

A system of alternate oppositely charged particles is most stable when it occupies the smallest possible volume, since the positive and negative charges attract each other. Indeed, the lattice energy of a series of compounds having the same ionic charge is, to a first approximation, a function of the interionic distance (see Figure 16).

Frequently the volume of a crystal depends on the size of the large anions and in this case the compound occupies the smallest volume when the anions are close-packed (see Figures 17*a* and *b*). Two such arrangements are possible: *hexagonal close-packing* in which every alternate layer of spheres is superimposed (Figure 17*a*) and *cubic close-packing* in which only every third layer is superimposed (Figure

17*b*). The names arise from the fact that the first type of packing has a six-fold axis of symmetry whereas the second leads to a *face-centred cubic* arrangement. Thus one can easily recognize the oblique face-centred square lettered ABCDE between the two arrows in Figure 17*b*. Closer inspection reveals that in both types of packing there are tetrahedral and octahedral arrangements of spheres; the open spaces

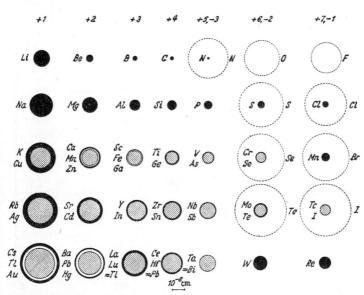

FIG. 15. Size of monatomic ions. (The symbols of the elements relate to cations having the charge shown at the top of each column; for multiple circles the elements are given in order of decreasing ionic diameter.)

between the spheres can then be described as *tetrahedral holes* or *octahedral holes* and it is clear that the octahedral holes are the larger. Hence if the close-packed spheres represent anions it is possible to place smaller cations in the tetrahedral holes and larger cations in the octahedral holes. There are as many octahedral holes as there are spheres and twice as many tetrahedral holes. Thus, if all the tetrahedral holes were occupied, the formula for the compound would be

$(A^+)_2 B^{2-}$ whereas the formula A^+B^- corresponds to half occupation, and $A^{2+}(B^-)_2$ to quarter occupation of the tetrahedral holes. Alternatively, if octahedral holes were being occupied, the formula A^+B^- would correspond to complete occupation, $A^{2+}(B^-)_2$ to half occupation, and $(A^{3+})_2(B^{2-})_3$ to two-thirds occupation, etc. For an incompletely occupied set of holes, layers of occupied and unoccupied

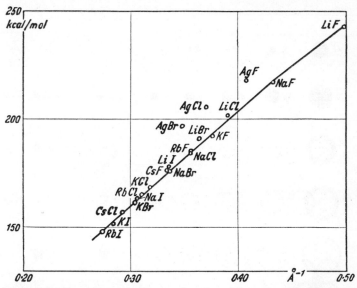

FIG. 16. Lattice energy of halides as a function of the reciprocal of the interionic distance.

holes can alternate thus forming a *layer lattice*. Table 2 summarizes the structures of several ionic compounds based on the close-packing of anions. The structures adopted are the ones in which the cations occupy the smallest possible holes, e.g. zinc sulphide has tetrahedral coordination, not octahedral, as in sodium chloride. From simple geometrical reasoning it is clear that there must be a critical value for the *radius ratio* r_+/r_- below which a given lattice type becomes unstable. For the sodium chloride structure the critical value is 0·41

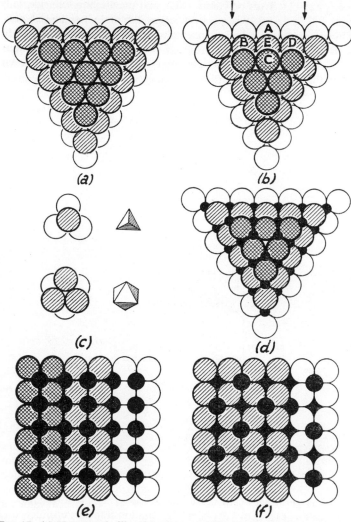

FIG. 17. (a) Hexagonal, (b) cubic close-packed, (c) tetrahedral and octahedral arrangements of spheres, (d) sodium chloride structure, (e) caesium-iodide structure, (f) calcium-fluoride structure.

(i.e. $\sqrt{(2)} - 1$). Thus beryllium oxide and magnesium telluride with $r_+/r_- = 0.26$ and 0.37 respectively crystallize in the tetrahedral zinc-blende type lattice whereas magnesium oxide and calcium telluride with $r_+/r_- = 0.59$ and 0.50 respectively crystallize in the sodium chloride structure. (Occasionally, however, a structure persists even when the critical radius ratio has been exceeded.)

TABLE 2

Crystal structures with close-packed anions

Holes	Occupancy	Symmetry	
		Cubic	Hexagonal
Tetrahedral	Full	O(Li,Na,K,Rb)$_2$ S(Li,Na,K)$_2$	
	$\frac{1}{2}$	ClCu BrCu I(Cu,Ag) S(Zn,Cd,Hg) Zincblende	O(Be,Zn) S(Zn,Cd) Wurtzite
Octahedral	Full	F(Li,Na,K,Rb,Cs,Ag) Cl(Li,Na,K,Rb,Ag) Br(Li,Na,K,Rb,Ag) I(Li,Na,K,Rb,Ag) O(Mg,Ca,Sr,Ba,Cd,Mn,Fe,Ni) S(Mg,Ca,Sr,Ba,Pb)	S(Fe,Co,Ni) AsNi
	$\frac{2}{3}$		α-O$_3$(Al$_2$,Fe$_2$,Cr$_2$,FeTi)
	$\frac{1}{2}$ (layer lattice)	Cl$_2$(Mg,Zn,Cd,Mn,Fe,Co,Ni) Br$_2$Cd I$_2$Ni	Br$_2$(Mg,Cd,Fe,Co,Ni) I$_2$(Mg,Ca,Cd,Pb,Mn,Fe,Co) S$_2$(Ti,Zr,Sn,Pt) (OH)$_2$(Mg,Ca,Cd,Fe,Co,Ni)
	$\frac{1}{3}$ (layer lattice)	Cl$_3$Cr	Cl$_3$Fe Br$_3$Cr I$_3$(As,Sb,Bi)
Tetrahedral + octahedral	$\frac{1}{8}$ $\frac{1}{2}$	(Mg,Mn,Fe,Co,Ni,Zn) O4(Al,Cr) Spinel	

Formulae in bold-faced letters represent standard structural types.

Still larger holes occur in the *simple cubic packing* of spheres (see Figures 17e, f) and this explains why caesium chloride, bromide, and iodide, which contain the large caesium cation, crystallize with eight-fold coordination. In the case of calcium fluoride the fluoride ions also form a simple cubic lattice but only half the holes are occupied by the calcium ions (see Figure 17*f*). It is interesting to note that, in the lattices of calcium fluoride and sodium oxide, the cations and anions are simply interchanged (fluorite and anti-fluorite lattices). Other compounds which adopt the caesium iodide and calcium fluoride structures are listed in Table 3.

TABLE 3

Crystal structures with simple cubic packing of anions

Occupation of holes	Full	Cl(Cs,Tl)
		Br(Cs,Tl)
		I(Cs,Tl)
	½	F_2(Ca,Sr,Ba,Cd,Hg,Pb)
		O_2(Ce,Hf,Th,U,Np,Pu)

The crystal structures of the two modifications of silica are also closely related to structures with close-packed anions, thus the β-crystobalite (cubic) and β-tridimite (hexagonal) lattices are obtained

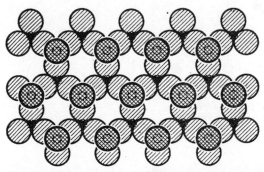

FIG. 18. Layers of oxygen and silicon ions in β-cristobalite and β-tridymite. (In tridymite the double layers are stacked to give hexagonal close-packing, in cristobalite they are displaced with respect to each other.)

by removing from alternate close-packed layers one-quarter and three-quarters of the oxide ions, and filling the remaining smallest tetrahedral holes with quadrivalent silicon ions as shown in Figure 18.

3

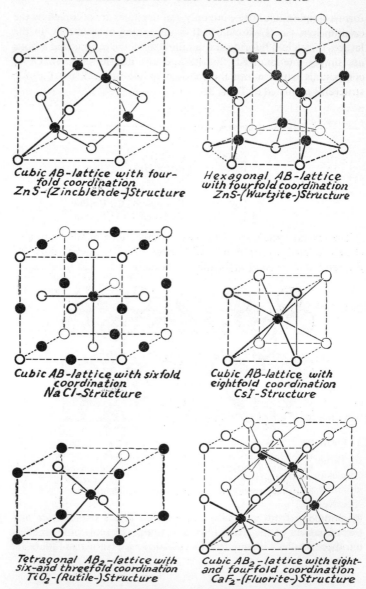

Cubic AB-lattice with fourfold coordination
ZnS-(Zincblende-)Structure

Hexagonal AB-lattice
with fourfold coordination
ZnS-(Wurtzite-)Structure

Cubic AB-lattice with sixfold
coordination
NaCl-Structure

Cubic AB-lattice with
eightfold coordination
CsI-Structure

Tetragonal AB₂-lattice with
six-and threefold coordination
TiO₂-(Rutile-)Structure

Cubic AB₂-lattice with eight-
and fourfold coordination
CaF₂-(Fluorite-)Structure

FIG. 19. Lattice types for AB- and AB₂-compounds.

A method of indicating the coordination ratios in crystal lattices has been devised by *Niggli* using chemical formulae of the type $ZnS_{4/4}$, $NaCl_{6/6}$, $CsI_{8/8}$, $CaF_{8/4}$, $SiO_{4/2}$, and $TiO_{6/3}$. The fractions, which are numerically equal to the suffix of the usual chemical formulae, give the *coordination number* of the first and second atoms respectively. However, it is more usual to represent lattice types by showing the position of each ion diagrammatically in three dimensions as in Figures 19 and 20.

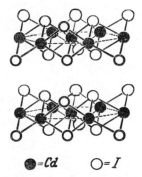

$\bullet = Cd$ $\bigcirc = I$

FIG. 20. Cadmium-iodide lattice.

The three-dimensional arrangement of ions in crystal lattices is also reflected in the *crystal habit* of ionic compounds which show the same symmetry relationships as the parent lattice. Thus, crystals which have cubic lattices crystallize in octahedra, cubes, rhombidodecahedra, or combinations of these.

3. Formation of molecules and complexes by ionic interaction

In Table 2, potassium sulphide and silver iodide were given as examples of compounds in which the anions are cubic close-packed and in which the cations occupy all, and half, of the tetrahedral holes respectively, i.e. $SK_{8/4}$ and $IAg_{4/4}$ in terms of the Niggli nomenclature. The iodide ions in crystalline stannic iodide are also cubic close-packed and the stannic ions again occupy tetrahedral holes but this time only one-eighth of the available holes are occupied. From the chemical formula $SnI_4 = SnI_{4/1}$ it can be seen that each anion has only one single cation as neighbour. As a result the cohesion of the anions through bridges of cations is lost and stannic iodide melts at 144°. Figure 21 shows clearly that in the lattice of stannic iodide there are small groups consisting of four anions and one cation. The formation of *discrete molecules* in this case therefore stems from the particular

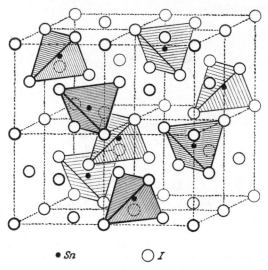

● Sn ○ I

FIG. 21. Lattice of tin (IV) iodide.

radius ratio of the ions and their coordination requirements. Just as the comparison $AgI_{4/4}$ and SnI_4 suggests reasons for the transition from an ionic to a molecular lattice, so the transitions $SiO_{4/2} \rightarrow SiF_4$ and $BN_{3/3} \rightarrow BO_{3/2} \rightarrow BF_3$ point to the formation of molecules of silicon tetrafluoride and boron trifluoride. It is apparent that molecules will always result when the number of anions is large in comparison to the number of cations and when the cations are so small that they are completely surrounded by the anions. A further example is gaseous sulphur hexafluoride.

The formation of *complex ions* can be considered similarly. Thus, when a ternary compound contains both small, highly-charged cations and large cations of low charge, it is frequently possible to distinguish in the lattice complex ions composed of the highly-charged cations as central ion surrounded by the anions as *ligands*. These ionic aggre-

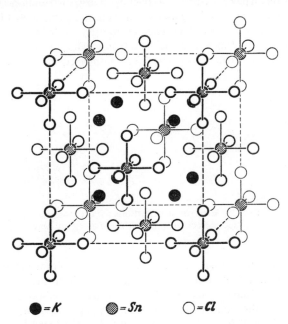

●= K ◉ = Sn ○ = Cl

Fig. 22. Lattice structure of the compound K_2SnCl_6.

gates survive when the lattice is destroyed by dissolution in a suitable solvent: e.g. the compound K_2SnCl_6, which can be considered to contain the ions Sn^{4+}, K^+, and Cl^-, dissolves in water to give potassium ions and complex ions of formula $SnCl_6^{2-}$ (see Figure 22). The formation of complex ions in this and related cases arises from the fact that the attractive forces between the anion and the small highly-charged cation are much greater than those between the anion and the large cation of low charge, which the anion cannot approach so closely.

Compounds containing ions which do not possess a closed shell call for special attention. Such compounds include those of the transition elements in which the d-shell is being filled. It was evident from the discussion on pages 12-14 that a spherical charge distribution can only be obtained when the p- or d-electron shells are completely filled, or half-filled with one electron in each orbital. By contrast, the electron cloud corresponding to a single d-electron will have four protrusions and the cloud distribution arising from nine d-electrons, in which there

Fig. 23. Electron distributions for an atom with a single d-electron and with a d-electron hole.

is one electron less than the complete spherical d^{10}-configuration, will possess four indentations as shown schematically in Figure 23. The particular spatial orientation of these protusions or indentations is irrelevant if the atom or ion is located in a weak field or in no field at all. However, if it is surrounded by electrically charged ligands the stability of the system will depend on the particular orientation of the non-spherical central atom. Figure 24 shows a favourable and an unfavourable orientation of a single d-electron in the octahedral field of six negatively charged ligands; (only four ligands are shown, the other two being above and below the plane of the paper respectively). In the first case, the d-electron rosette is directed towards the spaces between the ligands and in the second towards the ligands themselves, so that in the first case the repulsion between the d-electrons and the ligand electrons is less than in the second case.

Reference back to Figure 9 shows that if the six octahedrally disposed ligands are located along the coordinate axes then there are three favourable orientations of the d-electron cloud: d_{xy}, d_{xz}, and d_{yz}. Since each d-orbital can be doubly occupied it is possible to accommodate a maximum of six electrons in these energetically favoured

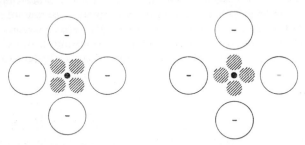

FIG. 24. Possible orientations of a d-electron in a ligand field.

d-electron states. The other two d-orbitals are energetically less favourable since the corresponding charge clouds extend towards the ligands. As a result, the five originally degenerate d-orbitals split under the influence of an octahedral *ligand field* into two new energy levels, a lower one which can accommodate six d-electrons and an upper one which can accommodate four d-electrons as shown in Figure 25.

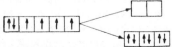

FIG. 25. Splitting of the d-electron energy levels in an octahedral ligand field.

Just as the ligand field can influence the orientation of the d-electron cloud so, by mutual interaction, can the d-electron cloud influence the spatial arrangement of the ligands. This can be illustrated by the stereochemistry of the cupric ion which has one d-electron missing from the complete shell (Cu^{2+}, $KL3s^2p^6d^9$): ligand-field theory explains the square-planar configuration of this ion in terms of the four ligands penetrating into the four indentations shown in Figure 23. Similarly, the d^8-configuration in the divalent ions of nickel, palladium, and platinum, stabilizes the square-planar configuration of complexes providing the occupied d-orbitals are each doubly filled.

The ligand field influences not only the configuration and stability (see page 82) of complexes but also their *magnetic properties* and colour (see page 100). For example, the magnetic behaviour of complexes of tervalent cobalt (Co^{3+}, $KL3s^2p^6d^6$) depends on whether the six d-electrons prefer to avoid each other by occupying all five orbitals thus reducing their mutual repulsion, or whether they prefer to avoid

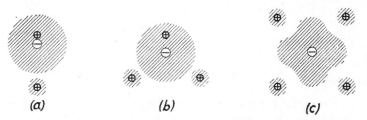

(a)   *(b)*   *(c)*

FIG. 26. Ionic polarization and ionic deformation.

the ligands by occupying the three energetically more favoured orbitals. Figure 25 indicates that the latter solution would be adopted in a strong ligand field when the separation between the two sets of energy levels is large; under these conditions the compound would be diamagnetic whereas in a weak ligand field it would be paramagnetic. Examples of these two situations are provided by the complexes $K_3[Co(NCS)_6]$ which is diamagnetic and $K_3[CoF_6]$ which is paramagnetic.

Electron clouds are not rigid structures. All atoms and ions can be polarized or deformed to a greater or lesser extent and this is important in chemical bonding. The distortion of the electron cloud of an atom or ion in the field of one or several neighbouring ions causes a shift in the centres of gravity of the positive and negative charges and this sets up *electric dipoles* as shown in Figures 26*a* and *b*. Hence the expression *polarization*. The greater the degree of polarization caused by a given set of ligands the greater the polarizability of the atom or ion is said to be. It is important to distinguish between the polarization of an ion and ionic deformation, which arises when distortion of the electron cloud occurs in such a way that the individually induced dipoles cancel out as shown in Figure 26c.

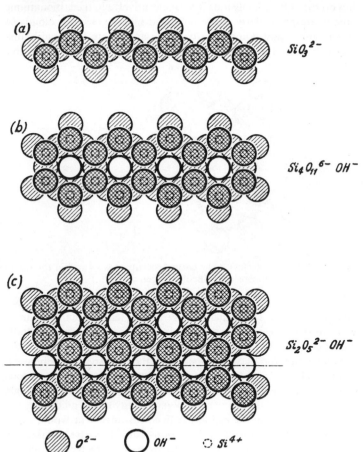

FIG. 27. Structure of silicate anions: (a) chain, (b) ribbon (e.g. asbestos), (c) sheet (e.g. clays, mica).

Polarization increases the attractive forces between cations and anions and causes them to approach each other more closely. Complex ions, in particular, produce conditions which favour ion polarization because of the one-sided unsymmetrical influence of the central ion on the individual ligands. Large, negatively charged, monatomic anions are particularly easily polarized but the electron clouds of small cations and complex polyatomic anions are less readily distorted because the central cations oppose the removal of negative

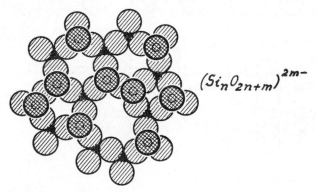

$$(Si_nO_{2n+m})^{2m-}$$

FIG. 28. Structure of glass. (The cations occupy spaces within the three-dimensional silicon–oxygen network.)

charge outward. This explains why anions tend to act as ligands, whereas only occasionally do polarizable cations behave as ligands, e.g. in complexes of the silver ion such as $[IAg_3]^{2+}(NO_3^-)_2$.

Polarization forces can compete with the repulsive forces between similarly charged ions to such an extent that one anion and two cations can form a triangular arrangement of bonds as in Figure 26b, the angle being more acute the greater the polarizability of the anion and the higher the charge of the cations. A linear arrangement would minimize the mutual repulsion of the cations but in this case polarization of the anion would be impossible, because of symmetry. Figures 26a and b show that polarization of the anion by one or two cations shifts the electron cloud of the anion in the direction of the polarizing ions and so reduces the force of attraction for further cations. Two important consequences of anion polarization are, therefore, unsymmetrical coordination and the reduction in coordination number of the anion. Both effects confer on ionic systems the characteristic features of covalent bonding which is treated in the next chapter, viz; saturation, directional properties, and the possibility of forming chains and rings of atoms or ions. The structures of silicates and glass shown in Figures 27 and 28 are typical examples. The preference that salts of the type AB_2 and AB_3 have for layer lattices is also explained by ion polarization.

4. The hydrogen molecule. Covalent bonding

Salts, and ionic complexes which are built up from monatomic ions, are really special cases within the vast array of chemical compounds Thus, for example, it was possible to say that in sodium fluoride half

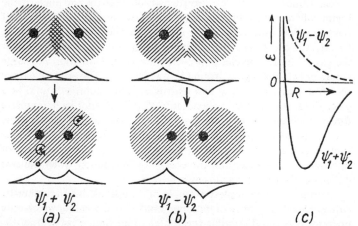

FIG. 29. Overlap of atomic hydrogen ψ-functions to give two molecular orbitals of the hydrogen molecule.

the electrons were associated with the sodium nucleus and half with the fluorine (see Figure 12); in general however, it is not possible to say which electrons belong to which atomic nuclei. As a rule only some of the electrons can be localized: these electrons together with the nuclei form the *atomic cores*, whilst the other electrons must be regarded as belonging to the whole molecule, or at least to a region extending over more than one atom.

The simplest case is that of the hydrogen molecule which consists of two hydrogen nuclei and two electrons. Figure 29a depicts the electron cloud of the hydrogen molecule in its ground state. The two electrons are spinning in opposite directions in accordance with the Pauli principle which also holds for molecules. The ψ-function for the electrons in the hydrogen molecule is obtained to a good approximation simply by adding the ψ-functions of the two atomic hydrogen electrons. It is also possible to subtract the two atomic ψ-functions (Figure 29b), but in this case the electron cloud is not capable of binding the nuclei together. The chemical forces which hold the two hydrogen nuclei together can be interpreted quite simply on this model since superposition of the two atomic ψ-functions leads to an appreciable increase in the electron density between the two nuclei in the region where both ψ-functions are large. By contrast, subtraction of the two ψ-functions reduces the electron density netween the nuclei. Clearly, the effect of superposition of the atomic ψ-functions is larger the closer the two nuclei approach since each ψ-function has large values only in the region around its own nucleus. The attractive force therefore increases as the two hydrogen atoms approach until at a given distance it reaches a maximum. With closer approach, repulsive forces between the two similarly charged nuclei and between the two inter-penetrating charge clouds predominate. In Figure 29c the energy of formation of a hydrogen molecule is shown as a function of inter-nuclear distance, and the energy of interaction when the two ψ-functions are subtracted is also shown.

Hydrogen is the simplest example of a molecule held together by *covalent bonding*. Covalent bonding, unlike ionic bonding which only operates between dissimilar species, can join similar as well as dissimilar atoms together.

5. Valency states and valency electrons

To extend the preceding treatment of covalency to more complicated systems it is necessary to introduce two further concepts: the *valency state* of an atom and *valency electrons*.

Valency states are not identical with the electronic states of an isolated atom (the so-called stationary states) with which we have so far
been concerned. Valency states are hypothetical situations which resemble the states of atoms in their compounds. In its valency state an
atom has one or more valency electrons. These are distinguished by
special distribution patterns and also by the fact that one cannot
attribute a definite spin orientation to them. Furthermore, valency
states are always singly occupied. Figure 30 shows schematically the
ground state of the sulphur atom and also a valency state with six
valency electrons. To understand the nature of covalent bonding in

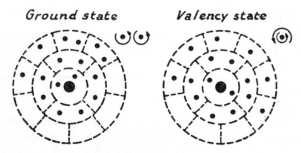

FIG. 30. Schematic representation of the ground state of the sulphur atom
and of its valency state with six electrons.

heavy atoms it is necessary to know the shapes of these valency electron clouds, i.e. their ψ-functions. Valency electrons can adopt the
same spherical, dumb-bell, or rosette-shaped distributions as atomic
s-, p-, and d-electrons and there is a further type which depends on
hybridization as discussed in section 8.

The formation of a molecule is considered to occur by the *overlap* of
the valency electron clouds of the atoms to form a molecular electron
cloud. The ψ-functions, or *molecular orbitals*, are obtained as in the
case of the hydrogen molecule by the addition, with suitable scaling
factors, of the ψ-functions (atomic orbitals) of the valency electrons.
These newly created molecular orbitals are arranged in an energy sequence which is again determined by the number of nodes, and they

become occupied progressively by electrons. As before, chemical bonding is explained by the increase in electron density between the atoms and there is a tendency towards maximum possible overlap of the valency electron clouds. In principle, a system of molecular orbital electron clouds extends over all the atoms which have supplied valency electrons, but it is usually simpler to break up the overall system into sections each of which extends over only two adjoining atoms. These *localized clouds* (or covalent bonds) arise from the overlap of the valency electron clouds of the two atoms concerned and occur in simple molecules such as H_2O, NH_3, and CH_4 and also in high polymers such as polyethylene $(CH_2)_n$.

6. Heterpolar covalent bonds

Covalent and ionic bonding are really limiting types of chemical interaction, and frequently intermediate types of bonding occur. For example among the chlorides of the first short period (LiCl, $BeCl_2$, BCl_3, CCl_4, NCl_3, OCl_2, and FCl) only LiCl approaches pure ionic bonding and NCl_3 pure covalency. The existence of intermediate bond types can easily be interpreted within the framework of our theory. Thus, in treating the hydrogen molecule, the molecular orbitals were obtained to a first approximation simply by adding together the atomic orbitals of the valency electrons. More rigorously, these atomic ψ-functions should first be multiplied by suitable factors which in the case of the hydrogen molecule are the same for both the 1s-atomic orbitals, However, if the bond is between two dissimilar atoms A and B with valency-electron functions ψ_A and ψ_B, then the molecular orbital is given by $\psi = \alpha\psi_A + \beta\psi_B$ where the coefficients α and β are both less than one.

If $\alpha = \beta$, and ψ_A is not very different from ψ_B then the two bonding electrons have approximately equal probability of being in the vicinity of the nuclei A and B and the bonding is said to be *homopolar*. If $\alpha > \beta$ then the electrons are more often in the neighbourhood of A; this leads to an acclumulation of negative charge around A and consequently to an excess positive charge at B since the charge on the nucleus of B is no longer fully compensated. In general, for $\alpha \neq \beta$ the centres of gravity of the positive and negative charges no longer coincide, an electric dipole is set up, and the bonding is said to be *heteropolar*. Finally, if $\beta = 0$, the electron pair is characterized by $\psi = \psi_A$ and spends all its time in the vicinity of A; this leads to the second limiting case: ionic bonding. The transition from covalent bonding through heteropolar bonding to ionic bonding is shown diagrammatically in Figure 31.

If two atoms in the same period form a bond then the one with the higher nuclear charge becomes negative, and the bond becomes more polar the further the elements are separated in the periodic table; e.g. the C—F bond is more polar than the C—O bond. On the other hand, if two atoms in the same group combine then it is the lighter element which becomes negatively charged, e.g. chlorine monofluoride is polarized in the direction Cl^+F^-. This tendency of an element to

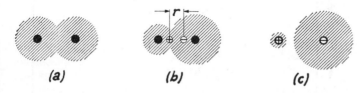

Fig. 31. Transition from covalent to ionic bonding.

attract electrons to itself in a compound is called the *electronegativity* of the element. It is more difficult to compare the electronegativities of elements which belong to different periods or groups, but the following method has been devised to achieve this. It is known that *bond strength* increases with increasing polar character. If the work required to dissociate two non-polar covalent compounds A–A and B–B is equal to E_{AA} and E_{BB} respectively then, as was first shown by *Pauling*, the work required to dissociate the heterpolar compound A–B is

$$E_{AB} = \tfrac{1}{2}E_{AA} + \tfrac{1}{2}E_{BB} + \Delta^2$$

where Δ is defined as the difference between the electronegativities of A and B. It is thus possible to set up an electronegativity series of the elements and this is shown in Figure 32. It is clear from this graph that most covalent bonds will be heteropolar.

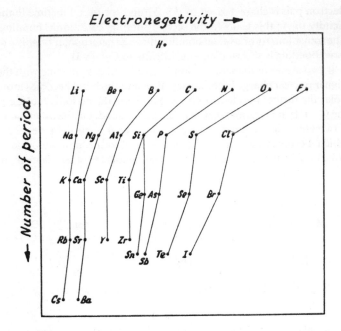

FIG. 32. Elements arranged according to their electronegativity.

7. The water and ammonia molecules. Polyatomic ions

To illustrate the process of bond formation, the formation of a molecule of water is shown diagrammatically in Figure 33. The two oxygen electrons in the valency state resemble those in the ground state except that, in the valency state, the spins of the two unpaired *p*-electrons can be either parallel or anti-parallel whereas in the ground state they must be parallel. In both states the two *p*-orbitals (shown schematically by the shading) are only singly occupied. Chemical bonds between the oxygen atom and the two hydrogen atoms arise from the overlap of the *p*-electron clouds with the *s*-electron clouds of the hydrogen atoms, so that each bond consists of a molecular orbital occupied by a pair of electrons; in other words, the number of bonds or the valency of the oxygen atom is given by the number of its valency electrons. The other electrons in the oxygen atom are not valency electrons and do not take part in bond formation; they are part of the atomic core.

The detailed structure of the water molecule is now well known: the O—H bond length is 0.98×10^{-8} cm and the angle between the two

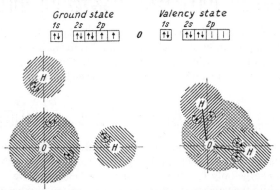

FIG. 33. Formation of O—H bonds in the water molecule.

O—H bonds is 104° 40′. This latter fact is readily explained by our model since the greater electronegativity of oxygen (see Figure 32) results in the presence of small residual positive charges on the hydrogen atoms which therefore repel each other and cause the bond angle between the two p-orbitals to increase from 90° to the observed value of 104° 40′.†

† Translators' footnote: An alternative interpretation of the bond angle can be given in terms of hybridization (see section 8): the oxygen atom is tetrahedrally hybridized; two of the sp^3-hybrids are occupied by pairs of electrons and the other two overlap with the hydrogen $1s$-orbitals at approximately the tetrahedral angle 109° 28′. The observed bond angle is slightly less than this because the mutual repulsion between the two pairs of non-bonding electrons, and between the non-bonding pairs and the bonding electrons is greater than the mutual repulsion between the two pairs of bonding electrons which are therefore pushed closer together. This also accounts for the similarity in the bond angles in H_2O, F_2O, and $(CH_3)_2O$ which is difficult to interpret on the simple electronegativity argument.

The shape of the ammonia molecule can be considered similarly.

In the same way, the formation of the pyramidal ammonia molecule arises from the tervalent valency state of the nitrogen atom in which the three *p*-electrons are oriented in three mutually perpendicular directions.

N, Ground state: $\begin{array}{c} 1s \\ \boxed{\uparrow\downarrow} \end{array}$ $\begin{array}{c} 2s \qquad 2p \\ \boxed{\uparrow\downarrow}\,\boxed{\uparrow\,|\,\uparrow\,|\,\uparrow} \end{array}$ *Valency state:* $\begin{array}{c} 1s \\ \boxed{\uparrow\downarrow} \end{array}$ $\begin{array}{c} 2s \qquad 2p \\ \boxed{\uparrow\downarrow}\,\boxed{\;|\;|\;|\;} \end{array}$

The case of the halogen hydrides is particularly simple since the halogens supply only one *p*-electron and this forms a bond with the *s*-electron of the hydrogen atom. Similarly the diatomic halogen molecules are formed by the overlap of two *p*-electrons.

F, Ground state: $\begin{array}{c} 1s \\ \boxed{\uparrow\downarrow} \end{array}$ $\begin{array}{c} 2s \qquad 2p \\ \boxed{\uparrow\downarrow}\,\boxed{\uparrow\downarrow\,|\,\uparrow\downarrow\,|\,\uparrow} \end{array}$ $=$ *Valency state:* $\begin{array}{c} 1s \\ \boxed{\uparrow\downarrow} \end{array}$ $\begin{array}{c} 2s \qquad 2p \\ \boxed{\uparrow\downarrow}\,\boxed{\uparrow\downarrow\,|\,\uparrow\downarrow\,|\,\uparrow} \end{array}$

It would seem at first sight that atoms with an even nuclear charge could have only 2, 4, 6, etc., valency electrons and those with an odd nuclear charge only 1, 3, 5, etc. since coupled electrons are *promoted* in pairs into the valency state. However, oxygen can also have an odd number of covalent bonds and nitrogen an even number, as exemplified by the ionic compounds Na^+OH^-, $Na^+NH_2^-$. Here oxygen and nitrogen are bonded covalently to hydrogen and ionically to sodium so that oxygen can be said to have a ligancy of one and nitrogen a ligancy of two, the term *ligancy* being defined as the number of atoms covalently bonded to the central atom. The variation in the ligancy of oxygen and nitrogen is easily explained: if the hydrogen atoms are homolytically split off from the ions OH^- and NH_2^- then the univalent anions O^- and N^- remain and these have a covalency of one less than the corresponding neutral atom because the number of unpaired *p*-electrons has been reduced by one, i.e. the ions O^- and N^- are *isoelectronic* with the atoms F and O respectively.

O⁻, Ground state = Valency state: $\begin{array}{c} 1s \\ \boxed{\uparrow\downarrow} \end{array}$ $\begin{array}{c} 2s \qquad 2p \\ \boxed{\uparrow\downarrow}\,\boxed{\uparrow\downarrow\,|\,\uparrow\downarrow\,|\,\uparrow} \end{array}$

N⁻, Ground state: $\begin{array}{c} 1s \\ \boxed{\uparrow\downarrow} \end{array}$ $\begin{array}{c} 2s \qquad 2p \\ \boxed{\uparrow\downarrow}\,\boxed{\uparrow\downarrow\,|\,\uparrow\,|\,\uparrow} \end{array}$ *Valency state:* $\begin{array}{c} 1s \\ \boxed{\uparrow\downarrow} \end{array}$ $\begin{array}{c} 2s \qquad 2p \\ \boxed{\uparrow\downarrow}\,\boxed{\uparrow\downarrow\,|\;|\;} \end{array}$

8. The methane molecule. Hybridization

The description of the bonding in methane is interesting in several respects and requires the introduction of two further concepts: the *excited valency state* and *hybridization*.

The molecular formula CH_4 indicates that the carbon atom in methane is 4-covalent since each hydrogen is known to form one covalent bond. However, as can be seen from Figure 34a the ground state of carbon, $1s^2 2s^2 2p^2$, has only two unpaired electrons, and the

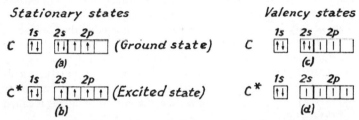

FIG. 34. Stationary states and valency states for the carbon atom.

corresponding valency state (Figure 34c) would therefore lead to a covalency of two. A valency state containing four electrons (Figure 34d) corresponds to the excited state $1s^2 2s 2p^3$ which is obtained by promoting one of the 2s-electrons into the vacant 2p-orbital (Figure 34b). Experience shows that, with very few exceptions, carbon compounds are derived from the 4-electron excited valency state which implies that the excitation energy of the carbon is more than repaid by the formation of the extra chemical bonds.

The question arises whether 6-covalent carbon compounds can be formed by a two-fold excitation process:

$$C^{**} \quad \boxed{1s} \quad \boxed{2s\ 2p} \quad \boxed{3s}$$

Excitation to C^{**} involves promotion of a 1s-electron to a 3s-level and this requires so much energy that it cannot be repaid by the energy of formation of two extra covalent bonds. It is, in fact, a general rule that valency electrons can only come from the same shell, or from two subshells of almost equal energy.

It might be concluded from Figure 34d that the four bonds emanating from the carbon atom in methane were of two sorts, one being formed by the overlap of the carbon 2s-electron with a hydrogen 1s-electron and the other three being formed by the 2p-electrons. Experimentally, however, no such differentiation is observed since the CH_4 molecule has the shape of a completely regular tetrahedron, all the hydrogen atoms being equidistant from the carbon atom and all mutually subtending the tetrahedral angle of 109° 28′. These facts can be interpreted by postulating that bonding in 4-covalent carbon involves a new type of valency electron distribution which derives from so-called q-orbitals. The q-orbitals are related to the familiar s-, p-, d-orbitals since we obtain the ψ-functions for the q-electrons by adding or subtracting the ψ-functions of s-, p-, and d-electrons of a given atom, the ψ-functions being first multiplied by suitable coefficients. The q-orbitals can therefore be regarded as mixtures or hybrids of the s-, p-, and d-orbitals, and the process of mixing is called hybridization.

Figure 35a shows how the combination of an s- and a p-orbital leads to two q-orbitals. In each case, the density of the q-electron cloud on one side of the nucleus becomes particularly large where the sign of the ψ-function of the p-electron is the same as for the s-electron so that the ψ-function of the q-electron builds up; on the other side the signs of the s- and p-functions are opposed and the q-electron charge density is correspondingly smaller. The same occurs for more complicated q-electron cloud distributions. As a result, an electron in a q-orbital moves predominantly on one side of the atom and so can penetrate more deeply into the charge cloud of another valency electron, thereby forming a stronger covalent bond.

Figures 35b–e show further possibilities of hybridization. The number of q-orbitals always equals the number of ψ-functions used in the hybridization. The q-orbitals created in this way are indicated simply by giving the direction in which the electron density becomes greatest. These directions are obtained by connecting the corners of a regular polygon (triangle, square) or polyhedron (tetrahedron, octahedron) to the centre of gravity which gives the position of the central nucleus.

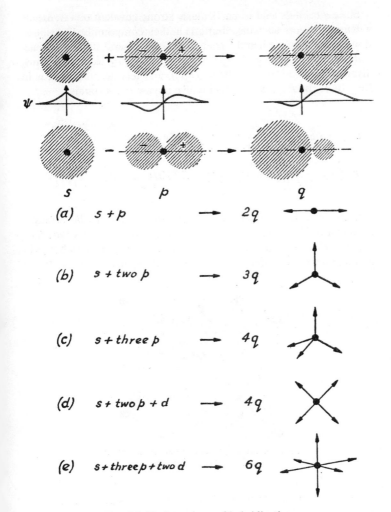

FIG. 35. Various types of hybridization.

Since q-orbitals lead to particularly strong covalent bonds, atoms will tend to adopt such distributions in their compounds. Hybridization always occurs when the transition from ground state to valency state involves a change in the number of valency electrons. Thus, divalent beryllium (e.g. in $Be(C_2H_5)_2$), and tervalent boron (e.g. in BF_3, BCl_3, $B(OH)_3$, $B(CH_3)_3$) involve the use of q-orbitals.

Be, Ground state: 1s 2s 2p

Be^* Valency state: 1s 2s 2p

B, Ground state: 1s 2s 2p

B^* Valency state: 1s 2s 2p

In this way, it is possible to predict correctly the spatial arrangement of atoms in compounds. Thus, on the basis of Figures 35a and b it is clear that beryllium will have a co-linear arrangement of bonds in its compounds and that boron will be triangular. In view of the

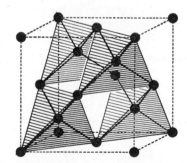

FIG. 36. Arrangement of carbon atoms in the diamond lattice.

preceding discussion of the methane molecule it is particularly noteworthy that hybridization of (s + three p) leads to four orbitals directed to the corners of a tetrahedron (Figure 39c). The hybridization (s + three p) is also found in other derivatives of quadrivalent carbon, e.g. CCl_4, $CHCl_3$, H_3CCH_3, diamond (structural formula $C_{4/4}$, see Figure 36), as well as in compounds of quadrivalent silicon, e.g. SiH_4, $SiCl_4$, $SiO_{4/2}$:

Si, *Ground state:*

Si^*, *Valency state:*

Finally, tetrahedral hybridization occurs in derivatives of the ammonium ion, NH^+, which is formed by combining a nitrogen cation, N^+, with four hydrogen atoms, since N^+ is isoelectronic with the neutral carbon atom:

N^{+*}

9. The ethylene molecule. Multiple bonds

In molecules considered so far, the number of valency electrons has always been twice the number of bonds between the atoms, and each bond was formed by two electrons which occupied the space between the bonded atoms. However, it is possible for more than two electrons to contribute to a bond and this is then called a *multiple bond*. If each pair of valency electrons is considered to form one bond then two electrons constitute a single bond, four a double bond, and six a triple bond. Very occasionally, bonding involves one, three, or five electrons.

It is convenient to regard the separate parts of the multiple bond as different from each other. The first part, the so-called σ-bond is cylindrically symmetrical about the direction of the bond and is produced by the overlap of s-, p-, or q-electron clouds, the possible combinations being $s+s$, $s+p$, $s+q$, $p+p$, $p+q$, and $q+q$. The second and third bonds are called π-bonds and have a nodal plane in the direction of the bond; they are normally formed by the sideways overlap of p- or d-electrons. Atoms of the first short period always use the combination $p+p$ whereas in higher periods the combinations

$p + d$ can also occur. Clearly σ- and π-bonds differ markedly in shape: the σ-electron cloud has no planar node, whereas the π-electron cloud has one planar node through the bond so that the Greek letters σ and π emphasize the similarity to s and p symmetries.

To gain a more thorough understanding of the nature of the double bond let us consider the ethylene molecule, C_2H_4, in which the atoms are arranged as follows:

$$
\begin{array}{ccc}
H & \cdot & H \\
 & C \cdot C & \\
H & \cdot & H
\end{array}
$$

Since each carbon atom is joined to three other atoms (C, H, H) each must be at least tervalent. This requires the excitation of one $2s$-electron into the vacant $2p$-orbital. As in the case of methane this leads to a four-electron valency state, but the four bonds formed are no longer equivalent. Thus, in ethylene, the s-electron and two of the p-electrons on each carbon are hybridized and used to form σ-bonds whilst the fourth electron remains in a p-orbital and is used for π-bonding as shown in Figure 37. Suppose that the p_x- and p_y-electrons hybridize with the s-electron and that the p_z-electron of each

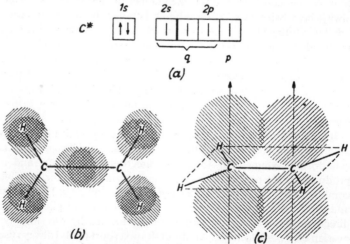

FIG. 37. Illustration of the bonding in ethylene.

carbon atom remains free; then the sp²-hybridization will lead to a planar system of electron clouds since the preferred directions of the two p-electrons lie in one plane (xy) and the s-electron has no preferred orientation. The three valencies therefore also lie in this plane and are directed at angles of 120° to each other (see Figure 37b). The p_z-electron clouds are perpendicular to this plane and, by their sideways overlap, form a π-bond as shown in Figure 37c. This overlap is greatest when all six atoms of ethylene are in one plane and becomes less if the two CH_2 triangles are twisted relative to each other about the C—C axis. There are thus only two orientations for maximum overlap. If the two carbon atoms carry different substituents, these two orientations lead to two isomers which differ in the geometrical arrangement of their atoms in space, e.g.

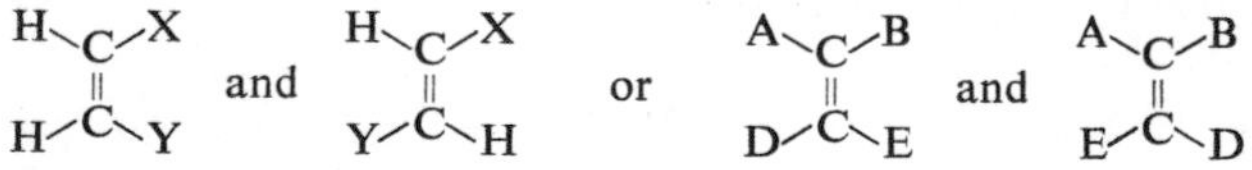

$$
\begin{array}{ccc}
\underset{H}{\overset{H}{\diagdown}}C\diagup^{X} & & \underset{H}{\overset{H}{\diagdown}}C\diagup^{X} \\
\parallel & \text{and} & \parallel \\
^{H}\diagup C\underset{Y}{\diagdown} & & ^{Y}\diagup C\underset{H}{\diagdown}
\end{array}
\qquad \text{or} \qquad
\begin{array}{ccc}
\underset{A}{\overset{A}{\diagdown}}C\diagup^{B} & & \underset{A}{\overset{A}{\diagdown}}C\diagup^{B} \\
\parallel & \text{and} & \parallel \\
^{D}\diagup C\underset{E}{\diagdown} & & ^{E}\diagup C\underset{D}{\diagdown}
\end{array}
$$

(*Cis-trans*-isomerism)

The acetylene molecule $HC \equiv CH$ can be described similarly. Here there is a triple bond between the two carbon atoms consisting of one σ- and two π-bonds. Each carbon atom has linear ($s + p$) hybridization

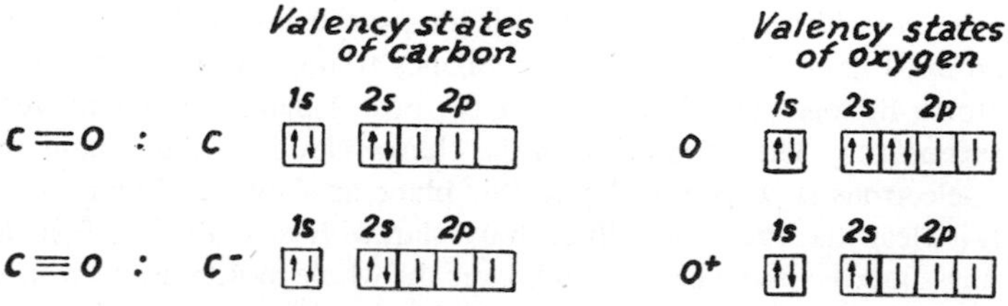

FIG. 38. Theoretical description of the bonding in carbon monoxide.

as shown in Figure 35a and this, by overlap with the two hydrogen 1s-electron, leads to the linear skeleton H—C—C—H. The two remaining p-electrons on each carbon atom form the two π-bonds.

The foregoing principles can readily be applied to the interpretation of multiple bonding in a variety of molecules. Thus in nitrogen, N_2, there is a σ-bond due to the end-on overlap of two p_x-electrons, and two π-bonds from the sideways overlap of two p_y- and two p_z-electrons. For carbon monoxide, CO, there is in addition to double bonding the possibility of triple-bond formation if one considers that the molecule can consist not only of the neutral atoms C and O but also of the ions C^- and O^+ which are each isoelectronic with the nitrogen atom. This situation is set out diagrammatically in Figure 38. Indeed, many of the physical properties which carbon monoxide and nitrogen have in common suggest triple bonding.

10. The benzene molecule. Delocalized bonds

The benzene molecule, C_6H_6, consists of six CH groups linked together to form a planar ring:

Each carbon atom has a coordination number of three, as in the case of the ethylene molecule, and again sp^2-hybrids form a system of σ-bonds with each other and with the s-electrons of the hydrogen atoms. Figure 39a shows that the valency triangles of the six carbon atoms fit together without strain to form a planar six-membered carbon ring. The orientation of the charge-clouds of the remaining p_z-electrons is perpendicular to this plane as shown in Figure 39b. It is clear that each p_z-orbital can overlap with two others to form a ring-shaped cloud which extends over the whole molecule and which is divided by the plane of the carbon ring into two equal parts. Various other combinations of the six p_z-orbitals are also possible and these lead to five further forms which are depicted together with the ring cloud in Figure 39c. To each of these distributions there corresponds an electronic state whose energy, as in the case of the hydrogen atom, is determined by the number of nodes. Figure 39c therefore

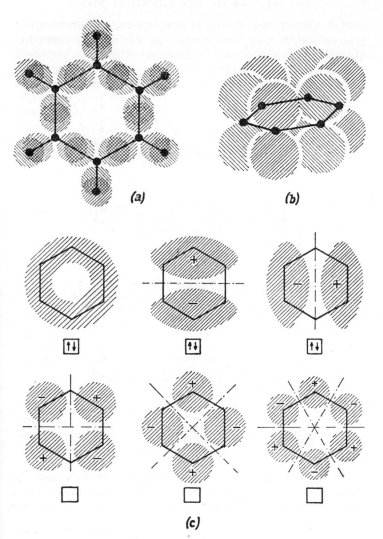

FIG. 39. Electronic states of the benzene molecule.

gives the electron states in order of increasing energy, there being two pairs with equal energy. In the ground state of benzene the three states of lowest energy are occupied by three pairs of electrons.

The preceding description of the benzene molecule implies that, in certain circumstances, the movement of the π-electrons is not restricted

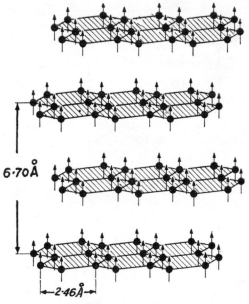

FIG. 40. The structure of graphite.
($\uparrow$ = orientation of the p-electron clouds)

to the space between two neighbouring atoms. In such cases the electron cloud cannot be assigned to one bond between a given pair of atoms and is said to be *delocalized*. It follows that structural formulae with localized bonds such as ⬡ and ⬡ do not represent the benzene molecule satisfactorily.

Benzene is by no means a unique example of this situation. Buta-
diene $CH_2{=}CH{-}CH{=}CH_2$, naphthalene ⬡⬡ , and many
other hydrocarbons with *conjugated double bonds* could be mentioned
and also graphite (see Figure 40). Delocalized double bonds always
occur when a structural formula can be written with the double
bonds distributed in more than one way.

Delocalized electron bonding is also characteristic of metals and
their alloys and these are discussed in sections 15 and 16.

11. Structural formulae with valency bonds

In the older valency theory stoichiometry was explained by assigning
a valency to each element. The molecular structure was then deduced
by writing down the chemical symbols in an appropriate arrangement
and connecting them with lines in such a way that the number of lines
coming from each atom equalled the valency of the element. Since
this method of writing chemical formulae leads to errors, *valency
lines* should only be used nowadays to indicate pictorially which
particular atoms in a molecule are directly joined together. Care-
fully used, they can also indicate localized valency bonds comprising pairs of electrons. The following formulae can be interpreted
in this way:

$$H{-}Cl \qquad \begin{matrix} H \\[-2pt] \diagdown \\[-2pt] H \end{matrix} O \qquad \begin{matrix} H \\[-2pt] | \\[-2pt] H{-}N{-}H \\[-2pt] | \\[-2pt] H \end{matrix} \qquad \begin{matrix} H \\[-2pt] | \\[-2pt] H{-}C{-}H \\[-2pt] | \\[-2pt] Cl \end{matrix} \qquad \begin{matrix} H\;H \\[-2pt] |\;\;| \\[-2pt] H{-}C{-}C{-}O{-}H \\[-2pt] |\;\;| \\[-2pt] H\;H \end{matrix} \qquad \begin{matrix} H \\[-2pt] \diagdown \\[-2pt] H \end{matrix} C{=}O \qquad \begin{matrix} F \\[-2pt] | \\[-2pt] F{-}P{-}F \\[-2pt] \diagup\;\;\diagdown \\[-2pt] F\;\;\;\;F \end{matrix}$$

They refer to hydrogen chloride, water, ammonia, methyl chloride,
ethyl alcohol, formaldehyde, and phosphorus pentafluoride.

However, the classical valency-line formulae are not always correctly interpreted in this way. For instance the formulae

$$Na{-}Cl \qquad Ca{=}O \qquad Ba{\Big\langle}\begin{matrix}O\\|\\O\end{matrix} \qquad Ca{\Big\langle}\begin{matrix}C\\\|\|\\C\end{matrix} \qquad Ca{\Big\langle}\begin{matrix}O\\ \\O\end{matrix}{\Big\rangle}C{=}O$$

are misleading because sodium chloride, calcium oxide, barium
peroxide, calcium carbide, and calcium carbonate are ionic compounds in which the metal atoms exist as cations. If the valency line is

used to indicate a covalent bond, as is normally done today, then the formulae should be written:

$$Na^{\oplus}Cl^{\ominus} \quad Ca^{\oplus\oplus}O^{\ominus\ominus} \quad Ba^{\oplus\oplus} \begin{matrix} O^{\ominus} \\ | \\ O^{\ominus} \end{matrix} \quad Ca^{\oplus\oplus} \begin{matrix} C^{\ominus} \\ \| \\ C^{\ominus} \end{matrix} \quad Ca^{\oplus\oplus} \begin{matrix} {}^{\ominus}O \\ {}_{\ominus}O \end{matrix}\!\!\diagdown C{=}O$$

On the other hand the formulae

$$H{-}O{-}O{-}H, \quad H{-}C{\equiv}C{-}H, \quad \begin{matrix} H{-}O \\ H{-}O \end{matrix}\!\!\diagdown C{=}O$$

are correct for hydrogen peroxide, acetylene, and carbonic acid because the hydrogen atoms are joined to the other atoms by covalent bonds. The improved valency formulae are sometimes called *structural formulae* because they correctly indicate the electron distribution within the compound.

Not only do the classical valency-line formulae fail to distinguish between covalent and ionic bonds but in some cases they also give the wrong value for the valency. This can be illustrated by considering a list of the various valency states of the atoms from lithium to chlorine. Such a list is given in Figure 41 which tabulates various series of isoelectronic atoms and ions. The chemical symbol is followed by the number of valency electrons and a description of their distribution in the valency state. The next column indicates the type of valency electron (s, p, q) and, finally, the number of electrons found in the outermost zone of the atom after bonding is given. This last number is obtained by doubling the number of valency electrons and adding to this the number of lone pair (or non-bonding) electrons which remain in the outermost shell.

If we now consider the classical valency-line formula for the salt sodium nitrate

$$Na{-}O{-}N{\diagup\!\!\!\diagdown}_{O}^{O}$$

two errors immediately become apparent. Firstly, sodium should not be linked to oxygen by a covalent bond and secondly, nitrogen cannot form five covalent bonds. This latter restriction is evident from Figure 41 and occurs because, for the first twenty elements, only electrons

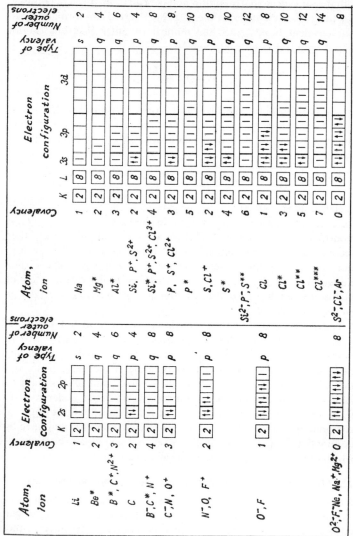

Fig. 41. Valency states of atoms and monatomic ions from lithium to chlorine.

with the same principal quantum number can be involved in bonding. For this reason elements in the first short period can form, at most, four covalent bonds since the number of outer electrons cannot exceed eight (the octet rule). Similarly,

$$H—O—N{\overset{O}{\underset{O}{\lessgtr}}}$$

cannot be regarded as the structural formula for nitric acid. Possible formulae for nitric acid and for the nitrate ion can be obtained, however, by taking the covalency of nitrogen to be either four or three:

$$H—O—\overset{\oplus}{N}{\overset{O^{\ominus}}{\underset{O}{\lessgtr}}} \qquad \overset{\ominus}{O}—\overset{\oplus}{N}{\overset{O^{\ominus}}{\underset{O}{\lessgtr}}} \qquad H—O—\overset{\oplus\oplus}{N}{\overset{O^{\ominus}}{\underset{O^{\ominus}}{\lessgtr}}} \qquad \overset{\ominus}{O}—\overset{\oplus\oplus}{N}{\overset{O^{\ominus}}{\underset{O^{\ominus}}{\lessgtr}}}$$

Such formulae imply that nitrogen cations N^+ or N^{2+} are involved in the covalent bonding, since oxygen, in the form of the anion O^-, is monovalent. However, these charges are not localized; usually they become more or less evened out by displacements of the electron clouds, and they are therefore called *formal charges*. The formal charges indicate the charges to be attributed to the valency state of each atom, and the sum of the formal charges equals the overall charge on the molecule, or molecule-ion.

The question as to whether there is a covalent bond and, therefore, whether a valency line should be drawn or not, is not always easy to answer, since there is frequently a transition between the two limiting cases of covalent bonding and ionic bonding. In inorganic chemistry, the valency line and particularly the double-bond lines should be used with caution since many compounds are better understood in terms of an electrostatic model. This restriction does not apply to compounds in which atoms of similar electronegativity are joined by essentially covalent bonds, i.e. to organic compounds and compounds which other non-metals form with each other.

12. Mesomerism. Canonical structures and conventional formulae

Reference to Figure 41 indicates that the classical line-formula of sulphuric acid is possible as a structural formula since sulphur can have a valency state with six unpaired electrons. However, other formulae are possible and these are given after the classical formula below:

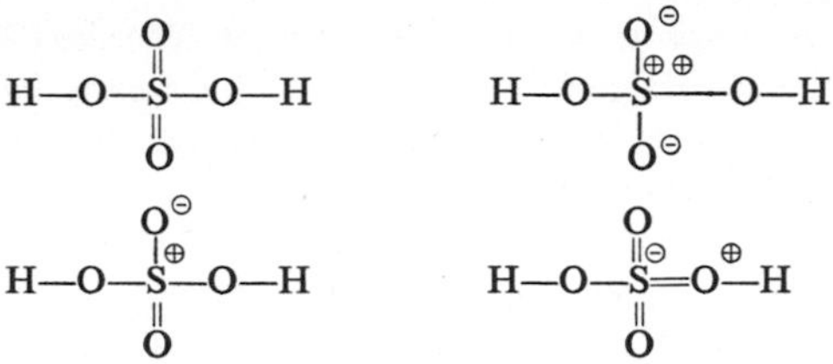

In many other cases several hypothetically possible valency formulae can be written and the question arises which should be regarded as the correct one. The answer is none, since all the possible valency formulae are necessary for a complete description of the bonding in a molecule. The benzene molecule again provides a good example. As shown in section 10 neither of the two Kékulé-formulae by itself

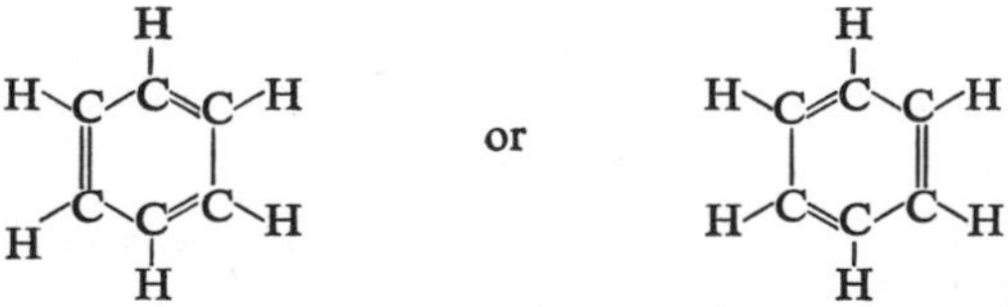

or

represents the actual bonding. Since each of the six π-electrons contributes to the bonding in the ring of six carbon atoms, and each σ-bond involves one pair of electrons there are, on average, three electrons in each C—C bond. The formula for benzene could therefore be written as:

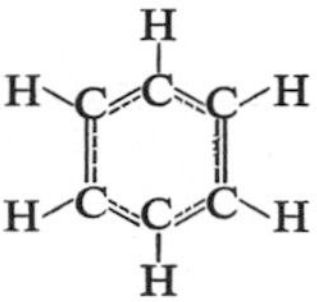

in which each broken line represents half a covalent bond. In the case of benzene such a formula represents the actual state of affairs reasonably well but in other cases valency splitting of this type leads to very complicated formulae. For this reason it is customary to retain the

5

full valency lines and to describe delocalized bonds by writing two or more valency formulae.

For benzene these are the Kékulé formulae. The situation is sometimes described by the term *mesomerism*, which means that the actual electron distribution lies somewhere between the electron distributions implied by the limiting formulae (*canonical structures*).

The number of theoretically possible valency formulae for a given molecule is often very large and it is therefore important, in practice, to select a single, reasonably adequate formula to describe the bonding. This can be termed the *conventional structure formula* of the compound.

The following rules are helpful in determining the conventional formula:

1. Atoms tend to form the largest possible number of bonds (*rule of maximum bonding*), but within the first period, the number of bonds cannot exceed four.
2. In covalent molecules, atoms tend to be uncharged (*electroneutrality rule*). The conventional formula should therefore have as few formal charges as possible.

The simplified scheme in Table 4 shows that the covalency always equals the classical valency if the formal charge is zero, in other cases the formal charge is most readily obtained by considering the charge

TABLE 4

Relation between covalency and formal charge for elements in the two short periods. (Figures to the right of the dotted line refer only to the second short period, those to the left apply to both periods)

Atom		Covalency							Atom
		1	2	3	4	5	6	7	
Li		0							Na
Be			0						Mg
B				0	-1				Al
C	Formal charge			(± 1)	0				Si
N			-1	0	$+1$	0			P
O		-1	0	$+1$	0		0		S
F		0		0		0		0	Cl

on the corresponding hydrogen-containing ion. Thus, monocovalent oxygen carries the formal charge of -1 because the corresponding hydrogen-containing ion is simply the negatively charged OH^- ion. Four-covalent nitrogen and four-covalent boron carry the formal charges $+1$ and -1 respectively because the corresponding hydrogen-containing ions are NH_4^+ and BH_4^- (cf. the compounds Na^+OH^-, $NH_4^+Cl^-$, and $Na^+BH_4^-$).

The simplest procedure for the construction of formulae is to combine all the atoms with single bonds at first and then to check whether the sum of the formal charges agrees with the overall charge on the molecule or ion. If this is not so, it is necessary to add double bonds and to check again. Below are a few examples of conventional formulae which can be obtained in this way:

Methane   Ammonium chloride   Methylamine   Methylammonium chloride

Boron trifluoride-ammonia   Carbon dioxide   Sodium azide

Thionyl chloride   Thionyl tetrafluoride   Calcium sulphate

Nitric acid   Disodium nitrosohydroxylamin-sulphate

If, for a description of the bonding, two or more formulae are required, they are shown connected by a *double arrow*. It is important not to read this as a chemical equilibrium between different molecular forms.

13. Multiple bonds

At first sight is seems remarkable that carbon dioxide is a gas whereas silicon dioxide is an involatile solid. Similar differences exist between various stoichiometrically identical compounds of homologous elements of the first and second short periods, e.g. nitric acid HNO_3 and metaphosphoric acid HPO_3. In all cases these differences in properties are due to differences in the constitution of the compounds. Carbon dioxide and nitric acid consist of discrete, kinetically free molecules whereas silicon dioxide and metaphosphoric acid are high polymers in which the atomic groupings SiO_2 and HPO_3 are further interlinked by means of ionic or heteropolar bonds:

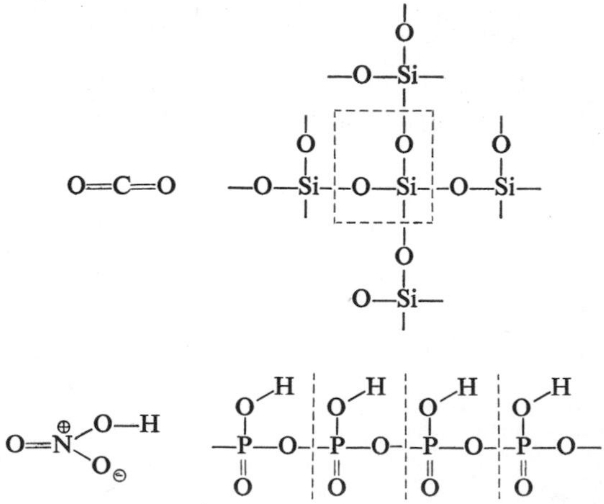

This behaviour reflects the tendency of atoms in the second short period and later periods to form fewer double bonds than their congenors in the first short period. Thus silicon has four single bonds rather than two double bonds and metaphosphoric acid, instead of being formulated as a monomer with two double bonds

$$O=P\underset{O}{\overset{OH}{<}}$$

should be written with only one, as above, or even with none at all:

$$
\begin{array}{cccc}
O\nearrow^{H} & O\nearrow^{H} & O\nearrow^{H} & O\nearrow^{H} \\
\underset{\ominus}{\overset{\oplus}{\underset{O}{|}}}P\!-\!O\!- & \underset{\ominus}{\overset{\oplus}{\underset{O}{|}}}P\!-\!O\!- & \underset{\ominus}{\overset{\oplus}{\underset{O}{|}}}P\!-\!O\!- & \underset{\ominus}{\overset{\oplus}{\underset{O}{|}}}P\!-\!O\!-
\end{array}
$$

This explains their *polymerization*.

However, boron, which belongs to the first short period, also shows a marked disinclination to form multiple bonds, so that boron nitride BN, and boric acid B_2O_3, as opposed to nitrogen, N_2, and dinitrogen trioxide, N_2O_3, are polymeric. Clearly, the greater polarity of the bonds to boron, which arises from the greater differences in the electronegativity of the combining atoms, opposes the formation of multiple bonds. This is not surprising since, with still larger polarity, even single covalent bonds are converted to a kind of bonding which leads to polymerization, namely ionic bonding. Further, as carbon and sulphur have approximately the same electronegativity it is understandable that sulphur dioxide consists of monomeric molecules like carbon dioxide. (The molecule might be formulated as $O=S=O$ but in view of the tendency to decrease the number of double bonds it is better to write it as:

$$\overset{\oplus}{S}\underset{\overset{\displaystyle O}{}}{\overset{\displaystyle O^{\ominus}}{<}} \longleftrightarrow \overset{\oplus}{S}\underset{\overset{\displaystyle O_{\ominus}}{}}{\overset{\displaystyle O}{<}}$$

This also emphasizes the stability of the eight-electron configuration and provides a further example of inorganic mesomerism). On the other hand, selenium dioxide, where the electronegativity difference is greater, is polymeric like silicon dioxide.

Other factors are also relevant in deciding whether multiple bonding occurs or not. This can be seen from the tendency of elements of the later periods to form large molecules with single bonds rather than small molecules with multiple bonds, even when electronegativity differences between the bonding partners is small: e.g.

O=O   S⟨S—S⟩S   N≡N   P⟨P—P⟩P

The absence of multiple bonds between the heavier elements can be attributed to the poor overlap of the p_π-electron clouds in the higher quantum shells and is indicated schematically on the left-hand side of Figure 42.

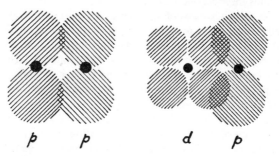

p   p   d   p

FIG. 42. Interpenetration of *p*- and *d*-electron clouds.

Polymerization of monomeric SiO_2- and HPO_3-units suggests that, in the later periods, only the *d*-electrons as distinct from *p*-electrons can be used for π-bonding. Figure 42 shows that the π-overlap of a *d*-electron and a *p*-electron is more effective than the π-overlap of two *p*-electrons. By considering possible valency states (see Fig. 41) it is easily seen that the following structural formulae are impossible.

O=Si=O,   H—O—P⟨O⟩,   H—O—P⊕⟨O⊖⟩

(Look up the valency states for the appropriate charge and coordination number and remember that silicon and phosphorus only form π-bonds with their d-electrons; Si and P^+ have no d-electrons and therefore cannot form double bonds; P* has one d-electron and can therefore form only one double bond). The mesomeric limiting form of a double bond involving π-overlap of a p- and a d-electron is the 'semipolar double bond' in which a single bond is superimposed on an ionic bond (cf. the canonical forms of the sulphuric acid molecule on page 57). It is noteworthy that double bonds with a p_π–d_π component differ from 'normal' double bonds which contain a p_π–p_π component in being unable to add on monovalent atoms or radicals to give single bonds.

14. Stereochemistry

In previous sections it has frequently been mentioned that the wave-mechanical model of the atom allows predictions to be made about the three-dimensional structure of molecules. Thus, the water molecule was bent rather than linear because of the orientation of its p-electrons; the tetrahedral structure of methane was interpreted in terms of its sp^3-hybridization, and the planar configuration of the six atoms in ethylene arose from p_π–p_π bonding between the carbon atoms, etc. Two more complicated examples can now be considered: carbonyl chlorofluoride, COClF, and thionyl chlorofluoride, SOClF. The classical valency-bond formulae

$$O{=}C{\overset{\text{Cl}}{\underset{\text{F}}{\big\langle}}} \quad \text{and} \quad O{=}S{\overset{\text{Cl}}{\underset{\text{F}}{\big\langle}}}$$

can also be considered as structural formulae. In their valency states carbon, oxygen, fluorine, sulphur, and chlorine are:

C*: $K2sp_xp_yp_z$ O: $K2s^2p^2{}_xp_yp_z$ F: $K2s^2p_x^2p_y^2p_z$

$\underbrace{}_{\sigma}\ \ \underset{\pi}{\downarrow}$

S*: $KL3s^2p_xp_yp_z\,d_{yz}$ Cl: $KL3s^2p_x^2p_y^2p^z$

$\underbrace{}_{\sigma}\ \ \underset{\pi}{\downarrow}$

It is clear that the CO π-bond is formed by two $2p$-electrons (C, $2p_z$ and O, $2p_z$); the SO π-bond, on the other hand, is formed from a d- and a p-electron (S, $3d_{xy}$ and O, $2p_z$). The three σ-bonds coming from the carbon atom involve $sp_x p_y$-hybridization of the carbon valency state whilst the three σ-bonds coming from the sulphur atom are all p-valencies. Hence in carbonyl chlorofluoride the carbon atom is in the centre of a triangle formed by the oxygen, fluorine, and chlorine atoms, whereas in thionyl chlorofluoride, the sulphur is at the apex of a triangular pyramid, the base of which comprises the oxygen, fluorine and chlorine atoms:

$$O{=}C\overset{\displaystyle Cl}{\underset{\displaystyle F}{}} \qquad O{=}\overset{\displaystyle S}{\underset{\displaystyle F}{|}}{\diagdown}Cl \qquad \text{or} \qquad Cl{\diagup}\overset{\displaystyle S}{\underset{\displaystyle F}{|}}{=}O$$

It follows that there must be a non-superimposable mirror image of the thionyl chlorofluoride molecule and the properties of the liquid compound suggest that these two sorts of molecules do actually exist.

15. The metallic bond

Metallic bonding occurs in the majority of elements. Two characteristic properties of metals (which comprise three-quarters of the elements in the periodic table) give valuable pointers to the nature of metallic bonding.

1. Metals are electron conductors, i.e. an electron which enters a piece of metal can leave it at an arbitrary place elsewhere; for instance it can enter at one end of a wire and leave it at the other end.

2. In the crystal lattice of a metal, each atom is surrounded by a large number of other atoms. In Figure 43 three typical metal structures are depicted. In the second, for example, each atom is surrounded by fourteen neighbours; the first eight form a cube and the remaining six, which are only 15 % further away, form an octahedron.

From the large electrical conductivity of metals it appears that at least some of the electrons can move freely through the bulk of the metal. Since even lithium crystallizes in a body-centred cubic lattice, it is clear that the atoms cannot be bonded to each other by localized electron-pair bonds, for in that case the lithium atom, which altogether has only three electrons, would have to supply eight or even fourteen valency electrons. The discussion of intermetallic compounds, which follows in the next section, shows that even metallic elements with high atomic numbers supply only very few valency electrons for bonding, and certainly not as many as there are coordination partners. The fact that, in a metal lattice, one atom can simultaneously interact with a large number of others can be explained by considering that metals constitute an extreme example of delocalized bonding.

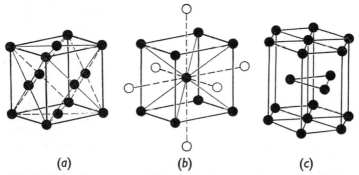

(a) (b) (c)

FIG. 43. Typical metallic structures: (a) face-centred cubic (cubic close-packed, α-phase), e.g. Cu; (b) body-centred cubic (β-phase), e.g. Li; (c) hexagonal close-packed (ϵ-phase), e.g. Zn. (The γ-phase has a complicated cubic lattice with 52 atoms in the unit cell.)

Conditions in metals are not as easily assessed as in benzene or polyene chains because metal lattices are three-dimensional structures.† However, several important results from the theory of metallic bonding can be understood on a highly simplified model in which the three-dimensional lattice is replaced by a one-dimensional system. Consider the formation of a linear array of lithium atoms from individual lithium atoms:

$$\text{Li} \longrightarrow \text{Li—Li} \longrightarrow \text{Li—Li—Li} \longrightarrow$$
$$\text{Li—Li—Li—Li} \longrightarrow \text{Li—Li—Li—Li—Li} \longrightarrow \dots$$

The first stage is the formation of a lithium molecule Li_2 which is comparable to the hydrogen molecule H_2. The two lithium atoms are

† It is interesting in this connection that the theory of unsaturated aromatic compounds was developed from the theory of the metallic state.

bound together by a pair of valency electrons; each lithium atom supplies its 2s-electron which in the formation of ionic lithium compounds (e.g. $Li + Cl \rightarrow Li^+Cl^-$) ionizes completely. The next (hypothetical) valency state has too high an excitation energy for K-shell electrons also to take part in the bonding of the Li_2 molecule, and this molecule, which occurs in lithium vapour differs from the H_2 molecule only by its greater interatomic distance ($Li—Li = 2.67 \times 10^{-8}$ cm, $H—H = 0.75 \times 10^{-8}$ cm) and smaller energy of formation (Li_2, 26 kcal/mole; H_2, 102.7 kcal/mole). The large separation and the consequent reduction in bond energy are due to the size of the Li^+ atomic core.

Consider next the hypothetical linear molecule Li_3. As the valency-electron cloud is spherical the central lithium atom cannot give preference to either of its neighbours. This situation is similar to that of the carbon p_z-electrons in benzene. The three atomic valency-electron clouds overlap to form one continuous distribution and two others with nodes; i.e. three molecular orbitals in all. (In benzene the six p_z-orbitals gave six π-molecular orbitals). Figure 44 shows the molecular orbitals and energy levels of Li_2 and Li_3 and these can readily be extended to the Li_4 chain as shown.

As the length of the chain is increased the number of electronic states into which the atomic 2s-state splits also increases, the number of states always equalling the number of atoms. The same occurs when lithium chains are placed side by side or stacked on top of each other so that finally the space lattice of the lithium crystal is obtained. It is of great significance that these electronic states have energies which are bounded by an upper and lower limiting value (see Figure 45). Within these limits the states form an *energy band* of closely-spaced values (*N.B.* one gram of lithium contains nearly 10^{23} atoms). Similarly, energy bands can also result from p- and d-orbitals. The electronic states (orbitals) within an energy band are filled progressively by pairs of electrons in the same way that the orbitals of an atom were in accordance with the Pauli principle (see Part I, section 2, page 5). This means that for lithium the electronic states of the 2s-band will be exactly half-filled.

It is of interest to enquire why lithium atoms or Li_2 molecules combine to form a metal lattice. In the lithium lattice the smallest distance between neighbouring atoms is 3.03×10^{-8} cm which is larger

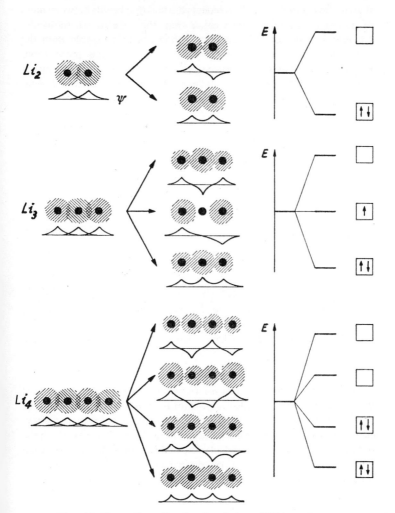

FIG. 44. Formation of molecular chains of lithium atoms.

than in the Li_2 molecule. This reflects the fact that bonds between pairs of atoms in the metal are weaker than they are in the molecule. Nevertheless the metallic form of lithium is more stable than the molecular form because, in the metal, one atom has many more neighbours than in the Li_2 molecule; as a result the binding energy per gram atom of lithium (i.e. per 6·92 g of lithium) is 39 kcal for the metal lattice but only 13·5 kcal for the molecule.

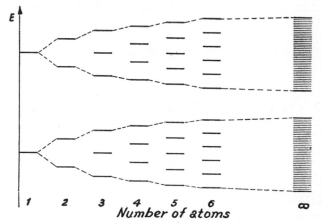

Fig. 45. Formation of energy bands by repeated addition of atoms to a system.

The possibility of hybridization (which first arises with elements of the first short period) is also important for the formation of metallic bonds. Thus strong bonds can be formed because the valency-electron clouds become concentrated along the direction in which the bonding partners are situated as indicated in Figure 46. According to Pauling the situation can be described by mesomeric limiting formulae just as in the theory of unsaturated carbon compounds:

$$
\begin{array}{lll}
\text{Li—Li} \quad \text{Li—Li} & \text{Li}^{\ominus}\text{Li} \quad \text{Li—Li} & \text{Li}^{\ominus}\text{Li} \quad \text{Li} \quad \text{Li}^{\oplus} \\
\text{Li} \quad \text{Li—Li} \quad \text{Li} & \text{Li} \quad \text{Li—Li} \quad \text{Li} & \text{Li} \quad \text{Li—Li} \quad \text{Li}^{\ominus} \\
\text{Li} \quad \text{Li—Li} \quad \text{Li} & \text{Li}^{\oplus} \text{Li—Li} \quad \text{Li} & \text{Li}^{\oplus} \text{Li—Li} \quad \text{Li}
\end{array}
$$

This is one reason why hydrogen does not form a metal since hybridization in this atom is impossible.

Since the appearance of bands of allowed energies is connected with the overlap of electron ψ-functions as shown in Figure 44, the width of each band will be a function of the crystal structure, because

 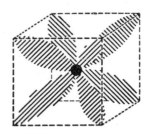

FIG. 46. Spherical electron cloud, and a rosette-shaped cloud formed by hybridization.

this determines the number of nearest neighbours in the crystal. Different metal atoms with the same valency, particularly elements in the same group of the periodic system, can often replace each other in arbitrary proportions without altering either the lattice type or the structure of the energy bands. This explains why such metals tend to form a complete series of solid solutions. Metallic alloys consist of such solid solutions or of heterogeneous mixtures of such solutions. Within certain limits even metal atoms of different valency can be interchanged in a lattice.

16. Intermetallic compounds

When one metal forms a *substitutional solid solution* in another the atoms are randomly distributed throughout the host lattice. At favourable ratios an ordered arrangement can be obtained leading to a system with a stoichiometric composition as indicated in Figure 47. At first sight the composition of these intermetallic compounds appears to be unusual and frequently quite arbitrary. For instance, copper forms the following compounds with zinc and tin:

$$CuZn — Cu_5Zn_8 — CuZn_3$$
$$Cu_5Sn — Cu_{31}Sn_8 — Cu_3Sn$$

Although the valency of the metal does not at first sight seem to have any influence on the composition of these compounds it does, in fact, play a significant part. The law of composition can be found by assigning to each metal the valency which it has in typical compounds with non-metals and then dividing the sum of the metal valencies by the total number of atoms in the chemical formula. In this way, by taking copper to be monovalent, zinc divalent, and tin quadrivalent, one obtains the following ratios for the foregoing compounds:

$$\frac{1+2}{1+1} = \frac{3}{2} = \frac{21}{14} \qquad \frac{5+16}{5+8} = \frac{21}{13} \qquad \frac{1+6}{1+3} = \frac{7}{4} = \frac{21}{12}$$

$$\frac{5+4}{5+1} = \frac{9}{6} = \frac{21}{14} \qquad \frac{31+32}{31+8} = \frac{63}{39} = \frac{21}{13} \qquad \frac{3+4}{3+1} = \frac{7}{4} = \frac{21}{12}$$

These same numerical ratios are also obtained in other cases; e.g. in the compounds Cu_3Al, Cu_5Si, Ag_3Al (21/14) and Cu_6Zn_6Al, $Cu_8Zn_2Al_3$ (21/13). These relationships were discovered by Hume-Rothery. *Hume-Rothery's rule* states that compounds having the same numerical ratio of valencies to atoms crystallize with the same lattice structure. Thus, the numerical ratio 21/14 (i.e. 3/2) corresponds to the *body-centred cubic* structure and the ratio 21/12 (i.e. 7/4) to the hexagonal close-packed lattice.

The composition of intermetallic compounds which has been systematized in this way can be satisfactorily explained in terms of the theory of metallic bonding developed in the preceding section. The valency of a metal in an intermetallic compound corresponds to the number of valency electrons which it contributes to the filling of the energy bands. In general, the electronic states comprising a given energy band cannot be filled to any arbitrary extent; as the electronic states become progressively occupied in their sequence of increasing energy a stage is reached at which the energy of electrons increases so rapidly that the atomic lattice becomes unstable. The numerical ratios which determine the lattice type of intermetallic compounds according to the Hume-Rothery rule lie between these critical values of the ratio of the number of valency electrons to the number of atoms.

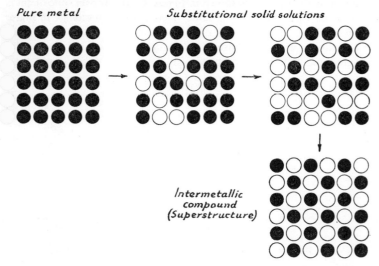

FIG. 47. Formation of an intermetallic compound from a solid solution of appropriate composition. (The transition can be effected by annealing the alloy.)

This theory explains the remarkable fact that the same sequence of alloy phases always occurs when one metal is alloyed to another of different valency. This sequence will now be discussed using the system copper–zinc as example. Copper has a face-centred cubic structure (see Figure 43a). When increasing amounts of zinc are added, the copper atoms are at first replaced by zinc atoms without affecting the face-centred cubic lattice. This is the so-called α-phase. Simultaneously however, the ratio of valency electrons to atoms is increasing because each zinc atom supplies two valency electrons. In pure copper this ratio is 1 : 1 because copper is monovalent in intermetallic systems. When the ratio has risen to 1·384 the α-phase becomes unstable and the system re-arranges at first partially and then completely to the body-centred cubic β-phase (β-brass) in which the first energy band can take up to $3/2 = 1\cdot5$ valency electrons per atom. Subsequently the β-phase is replaced by the γ-phase and this again by the ϵ-phase as shown in Figure 48. If however, one metal is replaced by another of the same valency, then no change in phase takes place since the ratio of valency electrons to atoms remains constant, e.g. the β-phases CuZn, AgZn, AuZn, and their solid solutions, and the γ-phases Cu_5Zn_8, Ag_5Zn_8, Au_5Zn_8, and their

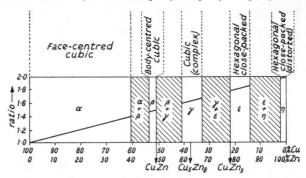

FIG. 48. Sequence of phases in the system copper–zinc.

solid solutions. It should be mentioned that certain transition metals with nearly full d-levels (e.g. Fe, Co, Ni, Rh, Pd, and Pt) behave as though they had a formal valency of 0 in intermetallic compounds; e.g. the compound Fe_5Zn_{21}

$$\left(\gamma\text{-phase, } \frac{0+42}{5+21} = \frac{21}{13}\right)$$

in which the iron atoms have an electron configuration $KL3s^2p^6\,d^8$.

17. Interactions between molecules. Dipole and dispersion forces. Ion dipole bonding

The three types of chemical bonding discussed in the preceding sections (ionic, covalent, and metallic) do not by themselves give a complete description of the interactions between atoms, ions, and molecules. The fact that neutral molecules like the inert gases can aggregate into crystal lattices at sufficiently low temperatures shows that there must be attractive forces even between uncharged particles with saturated valency electrons. Moreover, attractive forces in ionic lattices are frequently stronger than the purely electrostatic attraction between charged spheres. As early as 1873 *van der Waals* postulated the existence of attractive forces between all atoms and molecules, which led to the term a/V^2 in the equation of state that bears his name.

The so-called van der Waals bond, like the previous types of bond, is also fundamentally electrical in nature. Experience shows that materials comprising molecules in which the centres of gravity of positive and negative charge are non-coincident are harder to melt or evaporate than materials composed of molecules with no such dipoles. An example of this difference is given by the compounds:

$$
\begin{array}{ccc}
& \text{H} \quad \text{H} & \\
& | \quad\quad | & \\
\text{H—C—C—H} & & \\
& | \quad\quad | & \\
& \text{H} \quad \text{H} & \\
\end{array}
\qquad
\begin{array}{ccc}
& \text{H} \quad \text{H} & \\
& |\ominus \quad |\oplus & \\
\text{H—B—N—H} & & \\
& | \quad\quad | & \\
& \text{H} \quad \text{H} & \\
\end{array}
$$

Ethane, gas   Ammonia–borane, solid

Figure 49 indicates that intermolecular forces due to dipolar molecules can be attributed to electrostatic attraction between opposite charges just as in ionic bonds. Electrostatic forces between polar molecules

Fig. 49. Origin of the attractive force between two dipolar molecules.

increase with increasing dipole moment; the *dipole moment* is the product of the distance between the poles (centres of gravity of charge) and the magnitude of the charge on the poles (cf. also Figure 31).

A particularly important example of dipolar interaction is the *hydrogen bond* which occurs in many compounds containing O—H or N—H bonds and particularly in water.

It has been shown by *Debye* that the quantitative treatment of intermolecular forces must take into account the fact that dipole interaction can be increased by electrical induction when the electron cloud is sufficiently deformable or polarizable (see Figure 50). Furthermore, according to *London* (1930) the interaction between apparently dipole-free particles can be attributed to *induced dipole*

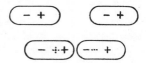

FIG. 50. Increase in dipole interaction by mutual induction.

interactions. Thus, the inert gas atoms appear to be spherical particles, each composed of a positive nucleus and negative electrons with coincident centres of charge because the extremely rapid movement of the electrons ensures that any charge separations which occur do so with equal probability in all directions from the nucleus, so that no method of measurement could detect the instantaneous electrical asymmetry. The dynamical picture of the rare-gas atom, as opposed to the static picture of the spherically symmetrical electron cloud, makes it possible to explain the attractive forces between them. If two or more rare-gas atoms (or any other atoms or molecules) approach one another, the nuclei and the electrons can form configurations over finite periods of time which lead to dipole attraction as shown

schematically in Figure 51. These attractive forces become particularly large when the outermost electron shell is occupied by many
electrons and its influence is increased by induction (deformation of
the electron cloud). Such dipole interactions arising from the extranuclear electron movements are closely related to the phenomenon of
dispersion, i.e. the resolution of multicoloured light into a spectrum
by means of varying refractive index. For that reason these attractive
forces are called *dispersion forces*.

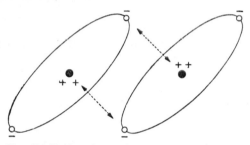

FIG. 51. Explanation of the attractive force
between two helium atoms.

It is interesting to compare the relative magnitudes of the different
types of van der Waals interaction with the total lattice energy of a
molecular compound and this again with the lattice energy of a typical
salt. This is done in Table 5. Van der Waals forces are generally much

TABLE 5
Origin of the lattice energy of molecular lattices (in kcal/mole)

	Dipole moment (in Debyes)	Static dipole interaction		Energy due to dispersion forces	Total lattice energy
		without polarization	with polarization		
Ar	0	0·000	0·000	2·03	2·03
H_2O	1·84	8·69	9·15	2·15	11·30
NH_3	1·50	3·18	3·55	3·52	7·07
HCl	1·03	0·79	1·03	4·02	5·05
HBr	0·78	0·164	0·284	5·24	5·52
HI	0·38	0·006	0·033	6·18	6·21
NaCl					184

smaller than the forces due to the other three types of chemical bond. This is because only residual charges – 'charge increments' – act on each other and because dispersion forces fall off much more rapidly than do coulombic forces with increasing distance. Nevertheless they can be quite appreciable in complexes composed of oppositely charged ions which approach each other much more closely than do uncharged molecules. The proportion of the total lattice energy due to dispersion forces is about 1–10% for alkali halide crystals but is

TABLE 6

Lattice energies of copper, silver, and thallium (I) halides and percentage due to dispersion forces

Compound	Structure	Number of outer electrons on cation	Lattice energy in kcal/mole	Percentage due to dispersion forces
CuCl	ZnS	10	222	6·8
CuBr	ZnS	10	216	7·0
CuI	ZnS	10	214	8·2
AgF	NaCl	10	218	10·9
AgCl	NaCl	10	206	14·2
AgBr	NaCl	10	202	14·0
AgI	ZnS	10	199	16·2
TlCl	CsI	12	170	16·5
TlBr	CsI	12	166	16·9
TlI	CsI	12	161	19·0

particularly large for the halides of univalent copper, silver, gold, and thallium where the cations have a filled d^{10}-configuration (see Table 6).

FIG. 52. Attraction between an ion and a dipolar molecule.

Ions and dipole molecules in appropriate orientations will also attract one another as shown in Figure 52; the attraction increases with increasing charge on the ion and with increasing dipole moment of the molecule. Many complex ions containing water or ammonia molecules as ligands can be considered as extreme cases of ion-dipole interaction, e.g.

$$[Cu(OH_2)_4]^{2+}, \quad [Cu(NH_3)_4]^{2+}, \quad [Co(NH_3)_6]^{3+}$$

The coordination number of the copper ion in the two examples shows that the ligand-field effect also occurs in ion-dipole complexes. The high solubility of many salts in water or other polar solvents is due to complex formation as a result of intermolecular forces between the ion and the solvent (*hydration, solvation*). During the dissolution of a salt in water the forces between oppositely charged ions in the crystal lattice are replaced by attractive forces between ions and dipoles and between the dipoles themselves (see Figure 53). On crystallization, some of the solvent molecules may remain chemically bound in the solid phase (solvate formation).

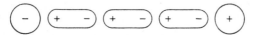

FIG. 53. Separation of ion-pairs by dipolar molecules.

It must always be remembered that several factors cooperate to form a chemical bond. At first sight it is difficult to understand why a complex between a metal ion and ammonia should be stable in aqueous solution since one would expect that water molecules with their large dipole moments would be more strongly held by the ions than are the ammonia molecules. However, in comparison with water molecules, ammonia molecules are more polarizable; consequently the dipole moment of an ammonia molecule is more readily enhanced on approach of a cation than is that of a water molecule. Below a critical distance, which is larger the higher the cationic charge, the dipole moment of ammonia might even be larger than that of water. Whether an aqueous solution of an ammonia complex is stable or unstable will therefore depend on whether the critical distance between ion and ligand can be attained or not. This explains why small divalent cations frequently form ammine complexes. By contrast, ammine complexes of the monovalent ions of copper, silver, and gold with fully occupied d-shells probably owe their stability to dispersion forces which are here particularly large because of the strong polarizability of the two bonding partners. Tervalent ions are usually precipitated as hydroxides by ammonia.

18. Chemical bonding and reactivity

(a) Ionic compounds and complexes

A chemical reaction can always occur if the atoms or ions of the original compounds can be re-arranged to give new groupings with stronger bonding. The question of reaction feasibility is therefore closely linked to the problem of chemical bonding. It is particularly easy to appreciate the conditions for reaction when only ionic bonds are involved. In this case, the most close-packed ionic arrangement gives the most stable configuration and one can therefore predict that compounds built up from ions will undergo reaction if one or more new compounds can be formed which have an overall *molar volume* smaller than the molar volume of the original compounds. (The molar volume is the number of millilitres occupied by the gram formula weight of a compound, i.e. the quotient of the gram formula weight and the density.) As an example, consider the reaction of potassium fluoride with magnesium fluoride to give potassium magnesium fluoride:

$$KF + MgF_2 \longrightarrow KMgF_3$$

	KF	MgF$_2$	KMgF$_3$
molar volume in millilitres:	22·8	19·6	38·6

The reason for the reaction is that potassium magnesium fluoride crystallizes in the particularly economical perovskite (calcium titanate) lattice shown in Figure 54.

On the basis of energy considerations it can be shown that double decomposition between various alkali halides having the sodium-chloride structure always gives those compounds in which the largest cation is paired with the largest anion and in which the smallest ions are joined together. Thus, double decomposition of lithium bromide and potassium fluoride (via their aqueous solutions) gives lithium fluoride and potassium bromide:

$$KF + LiBr \longrightarrow KBr + LiF$$

This can be seen as follows: let a, b, c, d be the radii of the ions K^+, Li^+, Br^-, F^-; then the energy of the reaction is proportional to

$$-\frac{1}{a+d}-\frac{1}{b+c}+\frac{1}{a+c}+\frac{1}{b+d} = \frac{(a+b+c+d)(a-b)(c-d)}{(a+d)(b+c)(a+c)(b+d)}$$

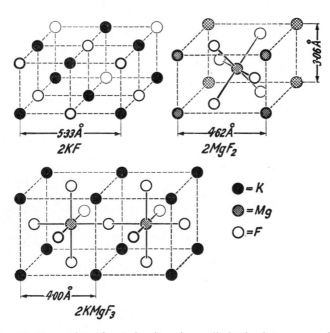

FIG. 54. Conversion of a rock-salt and a rutile lattice into a perovskite lattice: formation of $KMgF_3$ from KF and MgF_2.

since the lattice energy of each alkali halide is proportional to the reciprocal of its interionic distance (cf. Figure 16, page 22). As $a > b$ and $c > d$ the reaction under consideration leads to a gain in energy. Similarly in a system comprising two pairs of ions the two ions with the highest charge form one compound and the two with the lowest charge form the other crystal, since these pairings maximize the electrostatic attractive forces between the oppositely charged ions, i.e. $(Q_A^+ . Q_C^- + Q_B^+ . Q_D^-) > (Q_A^+ . Q_D^- + Q_B^+ . Q_C^-)$ providing $Q_A^+ > Q_B^+$ and $Q_C^- > Q_D^-$. For the same reason the smallest ions will combine with the highest opposite charge, the influence of charge being generally greater than that of ionic size. Several reactions may be mentioned as examples:

$$Na_2SO_4 + BaCl_2 \longrightarrow BaSO_4 + 2NaCl \quad (Q_{Ba}^{2+} > Q_{Na}^+, Q_{SO_4}^{2-} > Q_{Cl}^-)$$

$$2NaF + CaCl_2 \longrightarrow 2NaCl + CaF_2 \quad (F^- < Cl^-, Na^+ \sim Ca^{2+})$$

$$2AgCl + HgI_2 \longrightarrow 2AgI + HgCl_2 \quad (Cl^- < I^-, Ag^+ \sim Hg^{2+})$$

$$Na_2S + CaCO_3 \longrightarrow Na_2CO_3 + CaS \quad (S^{2-} < CO_3^{2-}, Na^+ \sim Ca^{2+})$$

[Leblanc – soda process]

Likewise, in the formation of ionic complexes and in their reactions, the most highly-charged cations will combine with the smallest anions:

$$K_3[FeCl_6] + 6KF \longrightarrow K_3[FeF_6] + 6KCl \quad (F^- < Cl^-)$$

That electrostatic forces frequently play a deciding role in the formation of ionic complexes can be seen from various stability series which show that, with increasing ionic size and increasing ionic distance, weaker (i.e. more easily dissociated) complex ions are formed. This rule is particularly well documented in cases when the central ion has an inert-gas configuration or is highly charged, e.g. the stability series:

$$AlF_6^{3-} > AlCl_6^{3-} > AlI_6^{3-}$$

$$FeF_6^{3-} > FeCl_6^{3-} > FeBr_6^{3-}$$

$$CeF_6^{2-} > CeCl_6^{2-} > CeBr_6^{2-}$$

Exceptions to this rule, which are not infrequent, show that other forces besides ionic attraction also play their part in crystal lattices. Examples of such exceptions are the reactions:

$$KBr + AgF \longrightarrow KF + AgBr \quad (K^+ > Ag^+, F^- < Br^-)$$

$$K_4[HgCl_4] + 4KI \longrightarrow K_4[HgI_4] + 4KCl \quad (I^- > Cl^-)$$

In the case of cations with a filled or nearly filled d-shell (e.g. Cu^+, Ag^+, Au^+, Tl^+, Zn^{2+}, Cd^{2+}, Hg^{2+}, Pt^{2+}) the stability of salts and complexes increases *not* with decreasing size of the anion but with its increasing polarizability, i.e. stability follows the sequence $F^- < Cl^- < Br^- < I^-$. Clearly, the reversal of the stability series in these lattices or complexes stems from the high proportion of the energy of formation which is due to polarization and dispersion forces. The low solubility of the silver halides and of the sulphides of metals with highly occupied d-shells is also due to dispersion forces; these are large in the case of easily polarizable anions such as Cl^-, Br^-, I^-, S^{2-} and outweigh the dispersion forces in solution where the cations are surrounded by

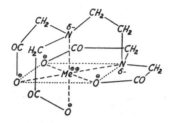

Fig. 55. Ethylenediaminetetra-acetic acid
complex of a metal ion.

water molecules which have a high resistance to polarization. The well-known group separation of sulphides in qualitative analysis is thus seen to depend on the action of van der Waals forces which sometimes tend to be neglected in considerations of valency and bonding.

Another interesting effect which leads to enhanced stability of complexes arises from the fact that an increase in the number of kinetically free particles leads to a gain in energy. As a result, ligands which can fill only one coordination position tend to be replaced by ligands which can occupy several coordination positions (*chelating ligands*). Metal complex ions formed by the hexadentate anion of ethylenediaminetetra-acetic acid give an impressive example of such chelation (see Figure 55).

Complexes of tervalent chromium and cobalt, divalent nickel, and di- and quadri-valent platinum resist ligand exchange. All these ions have incompletely filled d-shells:

$$Cr^{3+}: d^3, \quad Co^{3+}, Pt^{4+}: d^6, \quad Ni^{2+}, Pt^{2+}: d^8$$

It has already been shown on page 31 that this incomplete filling of the d-orbitals leads to electron clouds with six octahedrally arranged indentations (d^3, d^6-configurations) or four indentations in planar array (d^8-configuration). It is evidently difficult to eliminate the ligands (ions or dipolar molecules) from these 'holes' in which they are embedded. Figure 56 shows that, in the case of an incom-

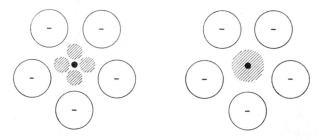

FIG. 56. Ligand substitution with and without a ligand-field effect.

pletely occupied d-shell, an unfavourable charge distribution ensues if one tries to insert a fifth ligand into a group of four in an attempt to replace one which is already there. With a spherical central ion, on the other hand, it is only necessary to shift the ligand along an equipotential surface. This ligand-field effect is today regarded as the main cause of the stability of the classical complexes of cobalt and platinum on which *Werner* developed his coordination theory.

(b) Covalent compounds

A system of covalent bonds is generally more stable the more bonds it contains, from which one can conclude that two single bonds are usually more stable than one double bond. This explains reactions based on an increase in the number of bonds such as

$$\begin{array}{ccc}
\text{H} & \text{H} & \text{H} \ \text{H} \\
| & | & | \ | \\
\text{H—C} \cdot + \ \cdot \text{C—H} & \longrightarrow & \text{H—C—C—H} \\
| & | & | \ | \\
\text{H} & \text{H} & \text{H} \ \text{H}
\end{array}$$

and

$$\begin{array}{ccc}
\text{H} \ \text{H} & & \text{H} \ \ \text{H} \\
| \ | & & |\ominus \ |\oplus \\
\text{H—B} + \text{N—H} & \longrightarrow & \text{H—B—N—H} \\
| \ | & & | \ \ | \\
\text{H} \ \text{H} & & \text{H} \ \ \text{H}
\end{array}$$

The polymerization of compounds with double bonds which is of such importance in the chemistry of plastics is a further illustration:

$$n \ \begin{array}{c}
\text{H} \ \text{H} \\
| \ | \\
\text{C=C} \\
| \ | \\
\text{H} \ \text{H}
\end{array} \longrightarrow -\left(\begin{array}{c}
\text{H} \\
| \\
\text{C} \\
| \\
\text{H}
\end{array}\right)_{2n}-$$

Ethylene   Polyethylene

If covalent bonds are split so that both the bonding electrons stay with one of the bond partners one speaks of *heterolysis*; if each moiety retains one of the bonding electrons we have *homolysis*. Non-polar covalent bonds usually split homolytically. An example is the high-temperature dissociation of the iodine molecule into iodine atoms: $I:I \rightarrow I \cdot + \cdot I$. An example of heterolysis is the dissociation of hydriodic acid in aqueous solution into iodide and hydrogen ions: $I:H \rightarrow I:^{\ominus} + H^{\oplus}$.

On the basis of Pauling's electronegativity scale we can predict that the most stable set of molecules which can be formed by pairs of covalent bonds will be achieved when the atoms of largest electronegativity difference are combined in one molecule, and those of most similar electronegativity are combined in the other molecule, since in this case the sum of the squares of the electronegativity differences is maximized. In other words, if A, B, C, D are four atoms of increasing electronegativity, then the distribution of bonds A—D and B—C is the most stable. With this knowledge many reactions involving bonds between elements of the first three periods can be understood. Some examples are listed in Table 7.

It is more difficult to assess the relation between reactivity and bonding when covalent bonds are converted into ions or ionic inter-actions as in the case of the protolytic dissociation of acids:

TABLE 7

Reactions interpreted on the basis of Pauling's electronegativity scale

$Cl-Cl+H-H \longrightarrow H-Cl+H-Cl$	$H \overline{H} \ \overline{Cl} \ Cl \longrightarrow H \overline{H} \ \overline{Cl} \ Cl$
$SiCl_4 + 4HOH \longrightarrow Si(OH)_4 + 4HCl$	$Si \overline{H} \ \overline{Cl} \ O \longrightarrow Si \overline{H} \ \overline{Cl} \ O$
$BH_3 + 3HOH \longrightarrow B(OH)_3 + 6H_2$	$B \overline{H} \ \underline{H} \ O \longrightarrow B \overline{H} \ \underline{H} \ O$
$NH_3 + 3HOCl \longrightarrow NCl_3 + 3HOH$	$H \ \overline{Cl} \ N \ O \longrightarrow H \ \overline{Cl} \ N \ O$
$ON.OH + HCl \longrightarrow ON.Cl + HOH$	$H \ \overline{Cl} \ N \ O \longrightarrow H \ \overline{Cl} \ N \ O$
$BF_3 + AlCl_3 \longrightarrow BCl_3 + AlF_3$	$Al \ \overline{B} \ \overline{Cl} \ F \longrightarrow Al \ \overline{B} \ \overline{Cl} \ F$
$BCl_3 + 3HF \longrightarrow BF_3 + 3HCl$	$B \ \overline{H} \ \overline{Cl} \ F \longrightarrow B \ \overline{H} \ \overline{Cl} \ F$
$PCl_3 + 3RC{\textstyle{O \atop F}} \longrightarrow PF_3 + 3RC{\textstyle{O \atop Cl}}$	$P \ \overline{C} \ \overline{Cl} \ F \longrightarrow P \ \overline{C} \ \overline{Cl} \ F$

$X-H \rightarrow X^- + H^+$. One might think that this heterolytic dissociation would occur with increasing ease the more polar the bond $X-H$ is. Indeed, the acidity of binary hydrides does increase with increasing electronegativity of the elements in a given period:

$$(CH_4 < NH_3 < OH_2 < FH; \quad SH_2 < ClH).$$

However, the opposite occurs for hydrides within a given group in the periodic table; here acidity increases with *decreasing* electronegativity of the elements

$$(HF < HCl < HBr < HI; \quad H_2O < H_2S < H_2Se < H_2Te).$$

In the second case the weakening of the covalent bond between hydrogen and the element, due to increasing size of the element, evidently outweighs the effect of the simultaneous decrease in electro-negativity.

Connections between the strength of oxy-acids and their molecular formulae are easily found. The fact that their strength increases with the number of oxygen atoms and decreases with the number of hydrogens can be explained by the change in size of the formal charges on the central atom in the polar limiting formulae. In this way the increase in the acidity in the series silicic acid < phosphoric acid < sulphuric acid < perchloric acid can be interpreted as an increased repulsion of the proton by the increasing charge on the central atom:

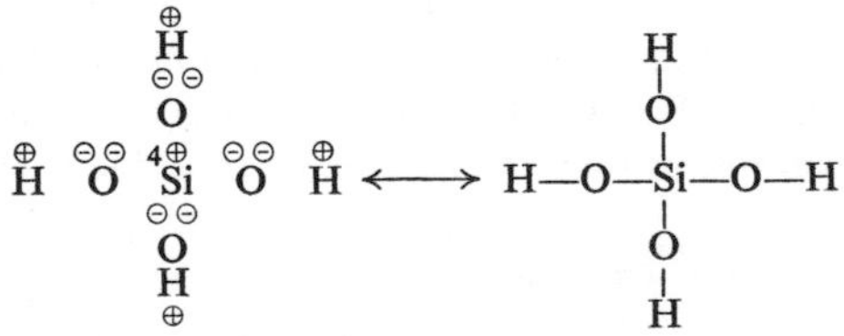

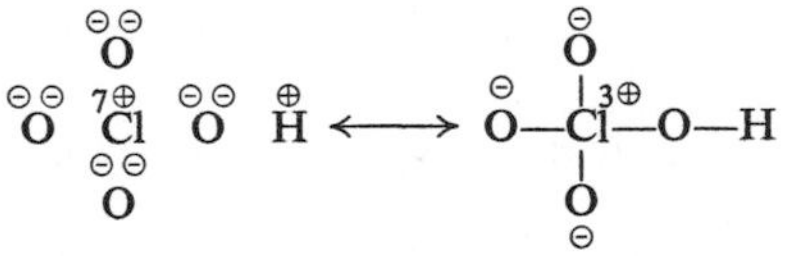

That anionic acids are weaker than neutral acids of the same electronic configuration can be attributed to the increased difficulty of separating a proton from a negatively charged particle, e.g. $OH^- < FH$; $SH^- < ClH$; $PO_4H^{2-} < SO_4H^- < ClO_4H$. Many reactions can be predicted in this way since weaker acids are liberated by stronger acids. It is thus possible to make a wealth of predictions starting from a few principles which emerge from the study of chemical bonding.

The course of many reactions is determined not so much by the stability of possible end products but by the energy required to form reaction intermediates since the velocity of the reaction will, in the first place, depend on the energy level of the *transition state*. Thus, for the double decomposition A—B + C—D $\longrightarrow$ A—D + B—C, an intermediate configuration

$$
\begin{array}{ccc}
 & B & \\
A & & C \\
 & D &
\end{array}
$$

('four-centre reaction') will be unfavourable because this arrangement demands a considerable lengthening of the bonds A—B and C—D (as well as of A—D and B—C) and all atoms would have abnormal valencies. A transition state involving only three atoms ('three-centre reaction') is considerably more favourable and hence so is a reaction A—B + C—D which can use such a transition state. A classical example of this is the hydrogen–chlorine reaction:

$$ Cl—Cl + \text{light (energy)} \longrightarrow Cl + Cl $$

$$ Cl + H—H \longrightarrow Cl...H...H \longrightarrow Cl—H + H $$

$$ H + Cl—Cl \longrightarrow H...Cl...Cl \longrightarrow H—Cl + Cl \quad \text{etc.} $$

The triggering of polymerizations by free radicals is explained similarly.

Conditions, of course, are particularly favourable for reaction if all atoms in the reaction intermediate exhibit their normal valency. An example of this is the hydrolysis of boron trichloride:

$$
\begin{array}{c}
\text{Cl} \\
\text{Cl—B} \\
\text{Cl}
\end{array}
+ \text{OH}_2 \longrightarrow
\begin{array}{c}
\text{Cl} \\
\text{Cl—B—O} \overset{\oplus}{\underset{\text{H}}{\overset{\text{H}}{<}}} \\
\text{Cl}
\end{array}
\longrightarrow
\begin{array}{c}
\text{Cl—B—O—H} + \text{Cl—H} \\
\text{Cl}
\end{array}
$$

In this connection it is interesting that hydrolysis of the B—Cl bond is prevented if the free coordination position of boron trichloride is blocked by a strong ligand such as trimethylamine: $Cl_3B—N(CH_3)_3$.

If several intermediate stages are possible, the actual course of the reaction is often decided by mesomeric stabilization. Thus, the preference for α-substitution in naphthalene can be explained by the fact that during the addition of a substituent, S, to an α-carbon atom a transition state is obtained which has seven mesomeric limiting formulae whereas for β-substitution the transition state has only six:

Many other problems of substitution in aromatic compounds can be treated in the same way.

The solution of problems of chemical reactivity frequently depends on one's skill in guessing correctly the reaction intermediates. Let us consider this aspect in a final example, viz. cationic substitution in a benzene ring which already has one substituent. Reactions of this type are nitration, nitrosation, sulphonation, and acylation. In these cases it is reasonable to assume a transition state in which the substituent has been added to one of the carbon atoms and its charge distributed over the ring:

It is important to note that the charge is not localized on a single atom in the ring; there are in fact three possible limiting formulae which place the charge on different carbon atoms:

If the benzene ring already carries a substituent (X_1), the alternating charge can only be *ortho*- or *para*- to the entering second substituent (X_2); this charge then coincides with the position of the first substituent in the case of *ortho*- and *para*-substituent but does not do so in the case of *meta*-substitution;

It will readily be appreciated that conditions favour the second substitution if a first substituent which lowers the ionization energy of the carbon atom (electron releasing substituent) is present in the *ortho*- or *para*-positions, or if a first substituent which increases the ionization potential (electron attracting substituent) is present in the *meta*-position. Electron-releasing substituents such as —CH_3, —NH_2, and —OH therefore direct cationic substitution into the *ortho*- and *para*-positions whereas electron-attracting substituents like —NO_2, —SO_3H, —CO_2H are *meta*-directing. The reduction in activation energy is particularly marked when the first substituent can accept the charge on the second substituent and simultaneously form a double bond with the ring:

This explains why aromatic amines and phenols are so readily substituted: since $-NR_2$ can be written as $=\overset{+}{N}R_2$ and $-OH$ as $=\overset{+}{O}H$.

19. Chemical bonding and mechanical strength

The type of chemical bonding within a compound not only determines its chemical behaviour but also its physical properties. Three of these properties, hardness, metallic conduction, and colour, form the subject of the concluding sections of this book.

Hardness is that property of a material which enables it to withstand the forcible intrusion of another object. Clearly hardness is an indication of the strength of the bonds between the atoms, since one material can only intrude into another if in the softer one chemical bonds are broken. The fact that diamond and ionic minerals such as calcium carbonate $Ca^{2+}CO_3^{2-}$ are hard confirms that both covalent and ionic bonds are difficult to break. Nor is it surprising that there is a connection between both ionic charge and ionic size on the one hand and the hardness of ionic materials of comparable lattice type on the other as shown in Table 8.

TABLE 8

Hardness of compounds with NaCl structure

Compound	Hardness	Interatomic distance	Compound	Hardness	Interatomic distance
NaF	3·2	2·31 Å	BeO	9·0	1·65 Å
MgO	6·5	2·10 Å	MgO	6·5	2·10 Å
ScN	7–8	2·22 Å	CaO	4·5	2·40 Å
TiC	8–9	2·16 Å	SrO	3·5	2·57 Å
			BaO	3·3	2·77 Å

7

Gases and liquids are extremely soft. These substances consist of molecules, i.e. atomic combinations which are held together within themselves by very strong bonding forces; but the forces between molecules themselves are small. Intermediate situations between these molecular systems and the three-dimensional network of covalent or ionic bonds (covalent or ionic lattices) are exemplified by macromolecular covalent chains and sheets of atoms. The structural formulae of some macromolecular substances of natural and synthetic origin are shown below:

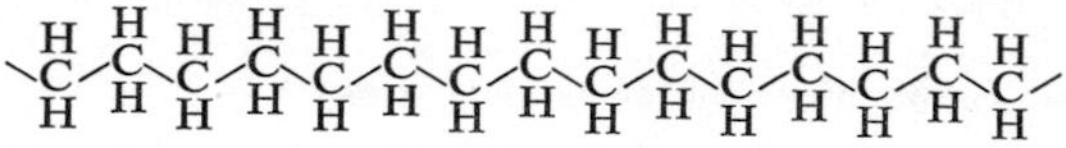

Polyethylene

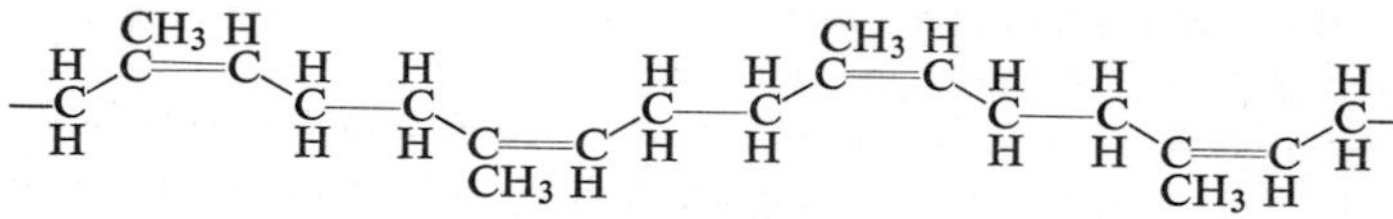

Natural rubber

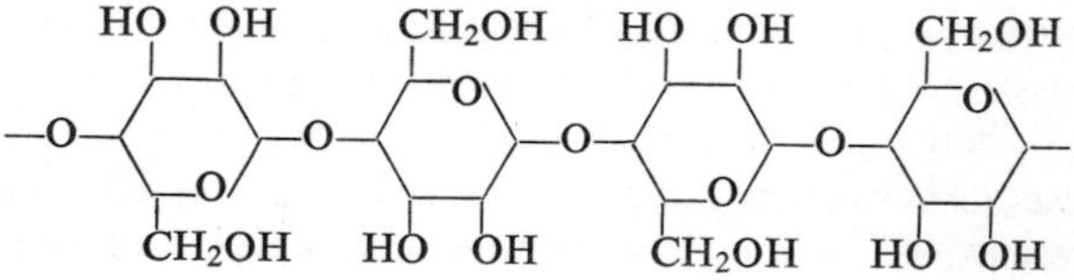

Cellulose

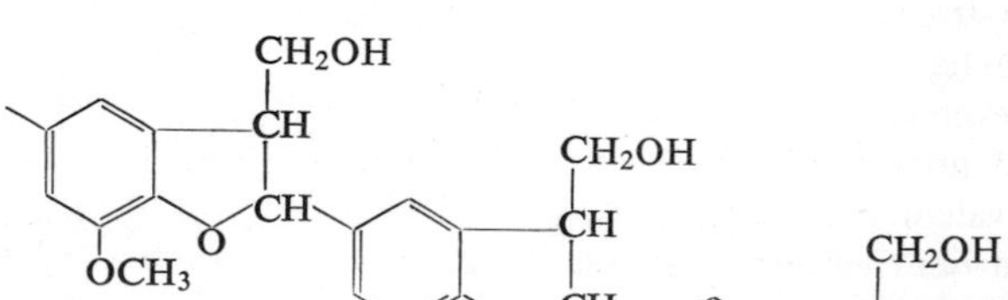

Lignin

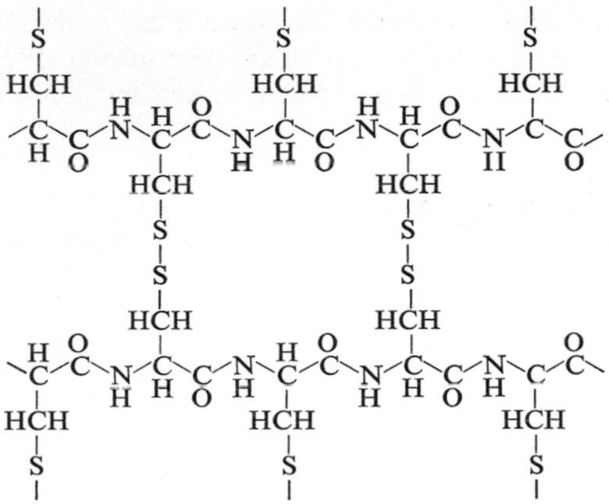

Keratin

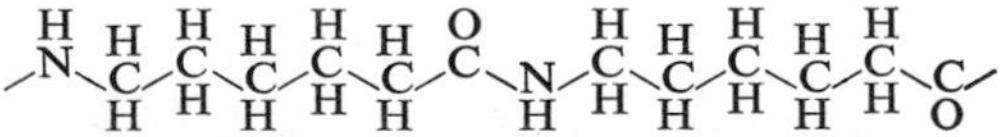

Nylon 6

In these materials identical atomic groupings are repeated indefinitely and the compound is stoichiometric. Repetitions of *identical* groups need not occur; for instance in the structure of proteins about twenty-five amino-acids take part as building units, and each type of protein has a given sequence of units.

If several chain molecules are arranged side by side or are intertwined, fibres are obtained which are flexible because the angle which the covalent bonds form with one another can easily be altered within certain limits. Rubber-like substances consist of networks of such chains knotted together. Figure 57 indicates how this leads to rubber-like elasticity.

Of the many substances with layer lattices we shall only consider graphite (see Figure 40) and sheet-like silicate structures. Figure 58 gives some idea of the structure of mica and clay minerals. That graphite and mica can be split into sheets is due to the fact that the bonding within the atomic layers is stronger than at right angles to these layers. Clay minerals owe their plasticity and ability to swell to

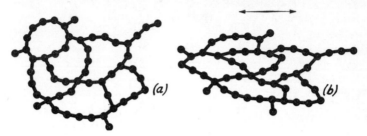

FIG. 57. Explanation of the elasticity of rubber-like substances.

the fact that water molecules can penetrate between the layers of silicon–oxygen rings; in the micas these layers are loosely held together by large cations of small charge.

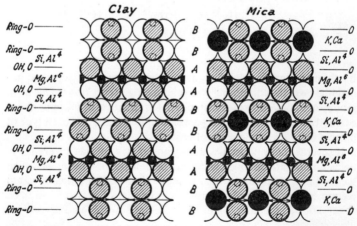

FIG. 58. Structure of micas and clay minerals of the montmorillonite type. (The section is perpendicular to the plane of the silicon–oxygen rings shown by the dashed line in Figure 27c.) Al^4 and Al^6 are 4- and 6-coordinate aluminium ions.

Similar principles determine the physical properties and hardness of metals. The characteristic feature of metallic bonding is that each atom is combined with a large number of others through weak delocalized bonds; this makes it particularly easy to deform the lattice structure of metallic crystals and leads to several characteristic properties of metals and their alloys; e.g. the possibility of plastic deformation through hammering, bending, rolling, pressing, etc. Pure metals, particularly in the form of single crystals, are outstandingly soft because in this case the atomic layers can glide over each other without hindrance. It is the aim of much industrial alloy

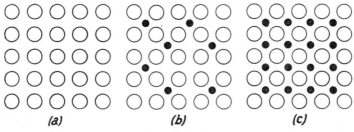

FIG. 59. Formation of an interstitial alloy (*b*) and an interstitial compound (*c*) from the host lattice (*a*).

production to change the plastic properties of metals in a given direction by incorporating 'impurities' into the metallic lattice; to this end the creation of phases containing *interstitial atoms* presents interesting possibilities. These phases arise through the introduction of small atoms or atomic cores into the interstices of a metal lattice as illustrated in Figure 59*b*. If such positions are occupied regularly an interstitial compound is formed (Figure 59*c*); typical examples are to be found among metallic hydrides, carbides, borides, and nitrides, which are all remarkable for their great hardness and extremely high melting point.

20. Metallic conduction

There is a close connection between metallic bonding and metallic conduction. The phenomenon of electron conduction in metals can be understood by comparing the crystal of a metal with an atom which has an incompletely filled electron shell, and a non-conductor or insulator with a rare-gas atom. This is done in the following example which is summarized pictorially in Figure 60: it is well known that

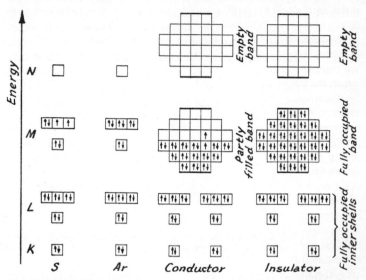

Fig. 60. Occupation of energy levels in conductors and insulators compared with the electron configuration of sulphur and argon atoms.

sulphur can be converted into sulphides from which it can be regained by oxidation. These processes involve the addition or removal of electrons:

$$S + 2e \longrightarrow S^{2-}, \qquad S^{2-} - 2e \longrightarrow S$$

Just as electrons can be added to or removed from the incompletely filled 3p-shell of the sulphur atom so electrons can be added to or removed from the incompletely filled energy band of a metal crystal. The difference between the two processes is that, in the case of sulphur, the addition and removal of electrons is restricted to the region around an individual atom, whereas in the case of a metal, the point where the electron emerges can be far from the point where it enters, since each electron cloud extends over the whole metal crystal (see Figure 44). Furthermore, electrons can readily be added to or removed from a metal because there are unoccupied electron states in the energy band immediately above the highest occupied level.

We can now appreciate under what conditions a material will be an insulator. Insulators are solids in which all the occupied energy bands are completely filled; they can be compared to the rare-gas atoms in which the electron shells are fully occupied. An example is provided by diamond in which the first energy band, with four electrons per atom, is just full, because each carbon atom provides four valency electrons.† The more free electron levels a crystal with an incompletely filled energy band contains the better it will conduct electricity. Hence the highest electrical conductivity is found in monovalent metals like copper, silver, and gold, because the first energy band of a cubic crystal comprising n-atoms can hold $2n$-electrons, whereas the monovalent metal provides only n-electrons. The corresponding electron-occupation is shown diagrammatically in Figure 60. Divalent metals, on the other hand, contain just enough electrons to fill the first band completely so that these elements would not conduct electricity if the first energy band were the only one occupied. However, the second band can also be occupied because it overlaps the first partially as a result of the similarity in energy of atomic s- and p-orbitals in the same shell. This situation is depicted in Figure 61. Since the energy rises quite rapidly during the occupation of the second band, divalent metals are not such good conductors as monovalent metals.

If the first energy band is just filled and the second one lies close to it but does not overlap, then only a small amount of energy is required to excite electrons from the first to the second band. Such energy can be supplied by the absorption of heat or light. If thermal energy promotes some electrons into the high-energy band the lower one will contain a corresponding number of holes. This results in a small conductivity which increases rapidly with temperature, i.e. the

† As the first energy band is fully occupied, diamond can also be regarded as a high polymer with localized electron-pair bonds.

material becomes a *semiconductor*. If promotion is due to light absorption the phenomenon is called photoelectric conductivity or *photoconductivity* as found in selenium and cuprous oxide.

One further point arises from Figure 60: thermal energy can also excite an electron within an energy band so that singly occupied electron states are found. This explains the weak paramagnetism of alkali metals, alkaline earth metals, copper, silver, gold, magnesium, and aluminium, since each unpaired electron produces a magnetic

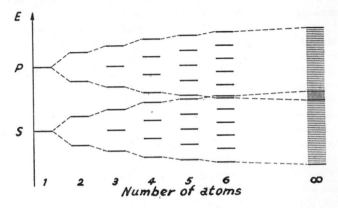

FIG. 61. Overlap of energy bands.

field as a result of its spin. In doubly occupied electron states the magnetic field of the two electrons cancel because they spin in opposite directions. The very high paramagnetism of the transition metals, which reaches its maximum in the case of iron (*ferromagnetism*), is due to incomplete occupation of the *d*-band.

21. Chemical bonding and colour

Colour results from the interaction of visible light with the material which appears coloured. In general, depending on their wavelengths, the electromagnetic vibrations which comprise the light wave will influence the movement of either the molecules themselves, or the atoms within the molecules, or the electrons. The detailed relations are shown in Figure 62. The differing action of light of different wavelengths arises from the fact that certain specific amounts of energy are

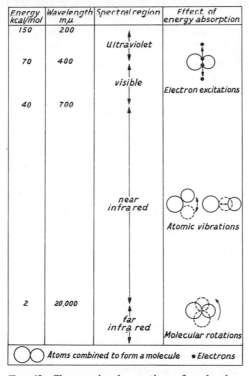

Energy kcal/mol	Wavelength $m\mu$	Spectral region	Effect of energy absorption
150	200		
		Ultraviolet	
70	400		Electron excitations
		visible	
40	700		
		near infrared	Atomic vibrations
2	20,000	far infrared	Molecular rotations

Atoms combined to form a molecule •Electrons

FIG. 62. Changes in the motion of molecules, atoms, and electrons due to absorption of light. (The energy required for each type of transition is given in kcal/mole. One mole. comprises 6×10^{23} particles.)

required for each specific alteration in the motion of a molecule, atom, or electron, and further, that the amount of energy which a light wave can transmit to an atomic or molecular particle is determined by its wavelength. (The energy $E = hc/\lambda$ where h is a universal constant, the *Planck quantum of action*; c is the velocity of light, and λ is the wavelength of the electromagnetic radiation.) The absorption of light is, in fact, a conversion of energy from one form to another in which the absorbed light (corresponding to the energy absorbed) disappears completely. To understand the origin of colour we must also remember that the white light radiated by the sun is composed of a spectrum of wavelengths in the region 400–700 mμ (1 mμ = 1/1,000,000 mm) and that smaller wavelengths ranges within this region correspond to definite colours. Furthermore, colours can be obtained not only by producing light of the appropriate wavelength, but also by absorbing from white light all the wavelengths except that of the desired colour. It is in this way, by the filtering out of 'complementary colours', that the colour of everyday objects is produced. Sources of coloured light, in which electrical or chemical energy is converted directly into light, are not relevant to our problem of the colour of compounds and will not be dealt with further. Absorbed light is not normally re-emitted as light but is converted into heat; however in *phosphorescence* and *fluorescence* it is partly or completely re-emitted as light.

The data in Figure 62 show that visible light has sufficient energy to excite the electrons of a molecule to higher energy levels. Simultaneously it is possible for small, partial amounts of the absorbed light energy to alter the *atomic vibrations* and *molecular rotations*. The energy diagram on the right-hand side of Figure 63 (which is composed of energy level curves like that in Figure 29) shows that excitation of the electron from the lower to the higher level not only alters the energy of formation of the molecule but also increases the interatomic distance. The horizontal lines drawn in the lower part of the curves show the energy of formation of the molecule for various vibrational states of the atoms. Still further lines should be drawn to indicate molecular rotations but these have been omitted for clarity. To understand how excitation of the molecule to a higher energy level can absorb green light, for example, the left-hand side of Figure 63 should be studied. The material under consideration will appear red because this is the mixed colour of those components of the light which are not absorbed, reflected, or transmitted. A further detail which is expressed in Figure 63 is that the energetically most stable state of the system corresponds to a state in which there are still

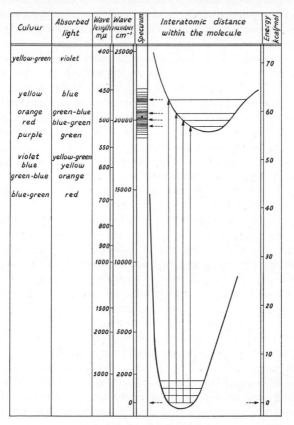

FIG. 63. Absorption of light.

vibrational motions; this is a consequence of the Heisenberg uncertainty principle according to which even atoms have a certain 'indeterminacy' or diffuseness regarding their positional parameters.

The excited molecule usually returns to the ground state by a *radiationless transition*; i.e. the excited electron returns to its normal level, during the collision of the molecule with another, non-excited molecule, the liberated energy being used to accelerate the molecular and atomic motions of the colliding particles. This means that heat is generated.

From the discussion so far, it is clear that an essential condition for the absorption of light of a given wavelength is that there is an energy gap of about 40–70 kcal/mole (cf. Figure 62). Another essential is that the distribution of centres of gravity of positive and negative charge (i.e. the dipole moment of the molecule) should change during the transition from ground state to excited state. This second condition can be explained by noting that an alternating electromagnetic field can only lose energy, i.e. do work, if charges are present which can be moved. The larger the alteration of the dipole moment in the transition to the excited state the higher is the *transition probability* and hence the intensity of the observed colour.

These simple rules enable us to determine whether a compound is likely to be coloured or not. In the field of ionic inorganic compounds, ions with rare-gas electronic shells such as Na^+, Ca^{2+}, Cl^-, O^{2-}, do not absorb visible light, and salts formed from such ions are colourless. We conclude that, in these compounds, either the lowest excited energy level is too high or, if it is sufficiently low, that the transitions are forbidden because they are not accompanied by a change in dipole moment. A different state of affairs obtains with ions of transition metals in which the *d*-shell is incompletely filled. The colour of compounds which contain these ions can be explained by the fact that the splitting of the *d*-levels in a ligand field gives low-lying excited states (cf. Figure 25). One can imagine that the colour of 6-coordinate tervalent titanium, Ti^{3+}, with an electron configuration $KL3s^2p^6d$ is due simply to the possibility of rotating the *d*-electron rosette into a less favourable orientation (cf. Figure 24).

The absorption of light energy can effect such a large separation of electrons from their atomic cores that it can lead to electron transitions between neighbouring atoms or molecules. An indication of such large transfers of charge is the unusual intensity of the ensuing *charge-transfer* absorption. This explains the observation that deeply-coloured compounds are obtained when oxidizable anions (i.e. anions which readily lose electrons) meet reducible cations (i.e. cations which readily accept electrons). The reverse combination of oxidizable cations and reducible anions also leads to colour. Interactions which lead to absorption of light are distinguished from normal redox reactions by the fact that the reaction products react with each other almost instantaneously to give the original system back again; the absorbed energy being evolved as heat. Illustrations are given by the following chemical reactions:

Complex	Colour	Reactions occurring during absorption of light
$[FeCl]^{2+}$	Yellow	$Fe^{3+}Cl^- \longrightarrow Fe^{2+}Cl$
$[FeSCN]^{2+}$	Red	$Fe^{3+}SCN^- \longrightarrow Fe^{2+}SCN$
$[FeOH]^{2+}$	Brown	$Fe^{3+}OH^- \longrightarrow Fe^{2+}OH$
$[CuCl]^+$	Green	$Cu^{2+}Cl^- \longrightarrow Cu^+Cl$
$[CuBr]^+$	Brown	$Cu^{2+}Br^- \longrightarrow Cu^+Br$

Normal redox reactions

$$\left. \begin{array}{l} Fe^{3+}+I^- \longrightarrow Fe^{2+}+I \\ Cu^{2+}+I^- \longrightarrow Cu^++I \end{array} \right\} \, 2I \longrightarrow I_2$$

The opaqueness of metals, even in very thin layers, implies that they absorb light completely; likewise when metals are finely powdered to prevent their polished surfaces from reflecting light they appear black. This follows from the fact that there are many vacant low-lying electron states within the incompletely filled electron energy band to which electrons can be excited by the incident light waves.

The colour of compounds containing deformed or polarized ions is due to the occurrence of *forbidden transitions* which become allowed because of the distortions. The yellow colour of many compounds of the easily deformed iodide ion is probably due to this. Transitions from ionic to low-lying metallic bonding states can also cause intense colour, e.g. black in sulphides such as PbS.

In covalent compounds, particularly in organic chemistry, colour always appears when extensive π-electron systems occur, since the π-electron cloud comprises several orbitals as outlined for benzene on page 51; the more π-electrons there are the closer become the occupied and unoccupied energy levels. The colour becomes particularly intense when atoms which can carry a formal charge participate in the formation of the π-electron system, since this increases the *transition moment*, i.e. the change in the dipole moment during the transition into the excited state. The formulae of nearly all natural and synthetic dyestuffs contain odd numbers of carbon atoms in chains or rings which have oxygen or nitrogen atoms at the end to act as charge carriers. The coupling of the π-electrons which are provided by the C, O, and N atoms can be described by mesomeric limiting formulae:

$$\overset{\ominus}{O}-CH=CH-\ldots-CH=O \leftrightarrow O=CH-CH=\ldots=CH-\overset{\ominus}{O}$$

$$R_2N-CH=CH-\ldots-CH=\overset{\oplus}{N}R_2 \leftrightarrow R_2\overset{\oplus}{N}=CH-CH=\ldots=CH-NR_2$$

$$\overset{\ominus}{O}-CH=CH-\ldots-CH=\overset{\oplus}{N}R_2 \leftrightarrow O=CH-CH=\ldots=CH-NR_2$$

Examples of dyestuffs which behave this way are given in the following diagram:

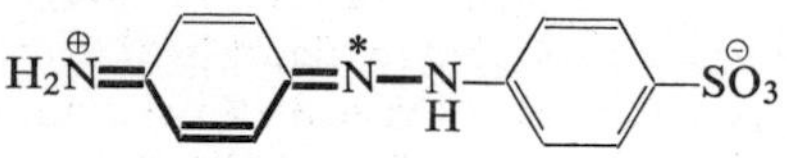

Methyl orange (acid form). (The nitrogen atom N* takes the place of a CH group in this case)

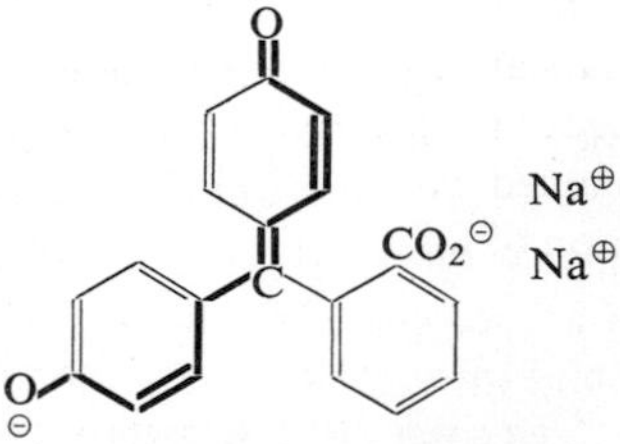

Sodium phenolphthalein

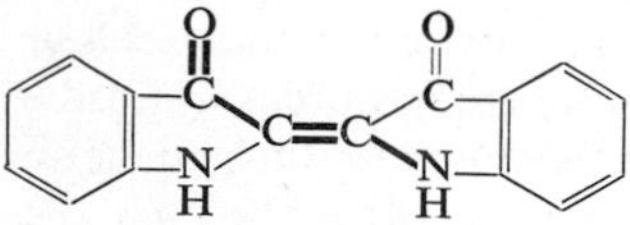

Indigo

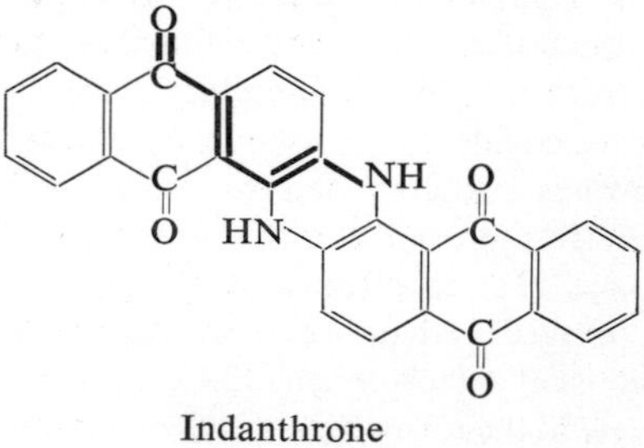

Indanthrone

Haem

The existence of these close relations between chemical constitution and the absorption of light allows predictions and deductions about chemical structures to be made. Indeed, our very thorough knowledge of the fine structure of atoms and chemical compounds has been obtained mainly by deductions made from observations on the interaction of light with matter.

Bibliography for Further Reading

ADDISON, W. E. *Structural Principles in Inorganic Compounds*. Longmans (1961).

CARTMELL, E., and FOWLES, G. W. A., *Valency and Molecular Structure*, 2nd Ed. Butterworths (1961).

COULSON, C. A., *Valence*, 2nd Ed. Oxford University Press (1961).

DUNITZ, J. D., and ORGEL, L. E., 'Stereochemistry of Ionic Solids', in *Advances in Inorganic Chemistry and Radiochemistry*, **2**, 1 (1960). Academic Press Inc.

EMELÉUS, H. J., and ANDERSON, J. S., *Modern Aspects of Inorganic Chemistry*, 3rd Ed. Routledge and Kegan Paul (1960).

EVANS, R. C., *An Introduction to Crystal Chemistry*. Cambridge University Press (1948).

GILLESPIE, R. J., and NYHOLM, R. S., 'Inorganic Stereochemistry,' *Quarterly Reviews*, **11**, 339 (1957).

GRIFFITH, J. S., and ORGEL, L. E., 'Ligand Field Theory', *Quarterly Reviews*, **11**, 381 (1957).

KETELAAR, J. A. A., *Chemical Constitution*. Elsevier (1953).

PAULING, L., *The Nature of the Chemical Bond*, 3rd Ed. Cornell University Press (1960).

SYRKIN, Y. K., and DYATKINA, M. E., *Structure of Molecules and The Chemical Bond*. Butterworths (1950).

WELLS, A. F. *Structural Inorganic Chemistry*, 3rd Ed. Oxford University Press (1962).

Index